MW01032087

Take Control Of Your Day

35 Time Management Habits & Techniques to Help Organize Your Life

ADESH SILVA

Quieting Your Brain

15 Techniques and Effective Habits for Stress Management in Everyday Life

Table of Contents

Introduction

Over half-a-million people die of heart disease every year. With one in four deaths tied to heart-related conditions, this has become the leading cause of death in the United States alone (CDC, n.d.).

You can eat all the healthy greens you want and exercise multiple times a day, but an often-overlooked cause of heart-related conditions is stress that goes unmanaged for far too long. Stress is also related to many other health conditions, such as anxiety or depression.

Stress has many different causes, but one thing we have to remember above all else is that it is natural. It doesn't feel great when we're experiencing it, but surprisingly, it can have some beneficial aspects when properly managed. It isn't a disorder, but a wiring built into the way that we think. It is a reaction to an outside threat. It is a chemical response that urges us to take action.

A happy life isn't one that is free from stress; it is one that involves the management of stress. The biggest reason that this type of worry can be so challenging to manage is because we don't understand exactly what stress is.

While stress does occur naturally, the negative side effects don't have to be a part of your everyday life. The solution to managing your stress is training your brain to think in a certain way.

Often, when people think about managing their health, their first thought might go to doctor's visits, medications, and other treatments. Luckily, stress management won't always require a prescription. Something as simple as laughing could help to drastically reduce your stress levels.

In fact, studies have proven that increased laughter helps to reduce the level of stress hormones present in your body, as well as the reduction of inflammation. On top of this, laughter can increase the good cholesterol in your body (Harvard Health Publishing, n.d.).

When stress goes unmanaged, it will affect every other part of your body. You can struggle with sleep, appetite, and mood control when worry is consuming every facet of your mind. Reducing stress isn't just good for your thoughts, but for your overall health.

There are plenty of other concerns that you might have in your life, so don't let stress be one of them. Constant worry could lead to anxiety, which could even increase symptoms of depression.

In this book, we are going to discuss the best methods and techniques that you can use to quiet your brain. This isn't about shutting out stressful thoughts and eliminating the worrying triggers in your life – unfortunately, we can't take your stressors away. There will always be work issues, monetary struggles, and relationship problems that you will just have to confront.

What we can promise to do is give you the resources needed to work through your greatest issues. We can provide you with what the body needs to feel relaxed and calm, even in the most challenging situations.

Each time you feel stress, you are doing damage to your body. Still, it can be hard for even the greatest medical professionals to link some of your health problems to stress, so it's important that we get it under control now.

There are enough issues in this world that could keep your worried mind busy for eternity. There will never be a lack of things to stress over. The urgency comes when we let this stress consume our daily thoughts, however. Our time on this beautiful earth is limited, so it's essential now that we learn to appreciate and enjoy each moment.

You are in charge of your own stress management, and your perspective plays a huge role in the thoughts and emotions that you have. What we have to remember is that each person is going to have their unique view on life. What stresses you out might not be a big deal to other people, and vice versa.

It's time now to take your own life into your hands. Now, more than ever, we have to put an emphasis on stress management. It seems normal to talk about health and nutrition, but what about the management of our emotions? What about the way that we experience and talk about our feelings?

It shouldn't be taboo to discuss the things that you feel. We can't be ashamed or afraid of the emotions that we have. When we pretend as though these are feelings that we can just stuff down and ignore, that creates an unhealthy mindset that will eventually show through your physical body.

Our minds can be like a bottle of soda. The more you shake it, the more it is going to explode when the top finally opens. The deeper you push your feelings down, the harder they are going to be to clean up once you finally let them out.

Think of it like a swinging pendulum. We always know that what goes up must come down. What we forget is that the harder it swings one way, the harder it swings the other. Pretending that everything is fine when it's not is only going to make those dark emotions feel even worse when you're forced to confront them.

Take action not just so that your day-to-day life is easier, but so you can live longer. Choose to manage stress for yourself, but for your friends and family, too. You want to be around them as long as possible. You should want to make the most of this life that you have been given!

There will always be things to cause you worry. There will still be hard days where you just want to give up. It is your mentality that is going to carry you through. It is the way that you think and feel that can be your greatest strength.

Stress is like a tool. Just like a hammer, you can either use this to build something great or you can let it be something that destroys everything around you.

Chapter 1

Identify Your Brain's Stress Response

The reason something like stress can be so challenging to manage is because we don't understand it. If you have a cold, you can take some medicine and have some soup. If you have a cut on your arm, you can put a Band-Aid on it. If you have chronic pain, you can take a hot bath or use a pain-relieving cream.

What do you do when your mind needs fixed? How can you heal the thoughts you have when the very thing that should be able to help you is where the problem starts? If we knew exactly how to manage our stress and the thoughts that we have, we wouldn't be stressed out at all.

Stress is something that is built into all animals. Humans are not the only ones to experience something like stress. It is a driving force that keeps us alive. If we never felt stress over anything, fear of the future and worry about what lies ahead, would we get anything done? Why would anyone go to work and operate within this society if we all just didn't care about anything?

Passion drives us, but even then it is connected to stress and worry. The same kinds of emotions which drive us towards what we love are helping to push us away from the things that we fear.

In this chapter, we're going to lay out what stress actually is. It is only once you begin to comprehend what your thoughts are and how your mind operates that you will know how to change it in your favor. Many individuals will go their entire lives living with fear and stress, all because they aren't aware that the tools to help alleviate those challenging emotions already exist within them.

We might be wired to have stress, but we are also wired to think logically in a way that helps to manage it.

Fight or Flight

As animals, we all have instincts that are naturally wired into us. These are responses and signals within our bodies that ensure our protection and survival. When you're hungry, you seek out food. When you're tired, you lay down and rest. When your stomach hurts, you go to the bathroom. These are instincts we never really had to be taught. We had to be potty-trained and taught how to eat, but we didn't have to learn that we *wanted* to eat. That has always just been a part of us.

One of these natural instincts is our fight or flight response. When you are presented with a stressor, you will either run from it or you will face it head-on. This isn't just an emotional reaction, either. It's a chemical process which occurs within your body. You will first notice that your breathing and your heart rate become faster. This is meant to help ensure we are prepared for anything that comes our way.

Your pupils will dilate and your mouth can become dry. You will have tense muscles and you may begin sweating. This is all caused by the release of cortisol – the stress hormone. Inside the body is gearing up for battle, too. Your adrenaline is released so that you can move quicker and more strategically. Your brain is kicked into high gear and you become hyper focused.

Imagine if the opposite occurred when presented with a threat! You would become sleepy and relaxed, unable to focus on anything that is going on. It is clear to see that this is a necessary process meant to keep you prepared for anything that comes your way.

Stressors come in all shapes in sizes. Some are physical threats – bugs, heights, thunderstorms, knives, guns, etc. Others aren't as easy to see – money, relationships, failure, bullying, etc. But no matter what type of stress you encounter, your body will react in the same way.

It will either choose to fight this threat or run from it. Some individuals are more naturally wired in one way rather than the other. Those who are more passive would be likely to flee from their threats, while others with a more aggressive outward personality might be more apt to fight. Of course, this reaction is determined by a number of factors, but it's essential that we know how we might be more inclined to behave.

Imagine a threat that you have faced, something which caused you to be afraid. How did you respond? Perhaps you had been called in for a one-on-one meeting with your boss. You might have been afraid over this, questioning if you were going to get reprimanded or written up. You might have fought this fear by confronting her and asking what the meeting was about, or maybe you used a flight response by avoiding the meeting and even coming up with an excuse to have to cancel it.

All animals have this response. An animal like a bunny would probably run from your approach, out of fear. An animal like a lion might attack you, a fight response.

The fight response isn't always so physical, either. You don't have to throw punches. Verbal fighting is also a response. One example is how many people don't handle criticism well. Whether they are being evaluated or called out for their actions, they might fight off the other person by yelling at them and disagreeing.

Similarly, flight responses aren't just found in the form of running away and hiding, either. Avoidance can be a flight response. Perhaps work drama leads to a trip to the bar after to drown the sorrows. Ignoring and blocking creditors who are looking for payment can be another flight response.

When you are confronted with a stressor, it's imperative that you evaluate the way in which you are responding. Are you facing this head-on and fighting in an aggressive way? Are you running and avoiding? By noticing your reaction, it can also be easier to determine the root cause of the problem. Let's take a further look at how you can properly reflect to determine the real issue underneath it all.

Reflecting on the Past

When figuring out where your thoughts and feelings started, we have to look towards the past. The things you experienced as a child created the individual that you are now. Of course, our minds are always changing, and we do have the power – at any time in our life – to alter the thoughts that we have. At the same time, younger minds are more susceptible, like sponges that soak up everything that comes their way.

These thoughts that you had during your childhood development are responsible for the groundwork and foundation of how you think and feel now. Even if you think completely differently than you did as a child and your beliefs are the exact opposite, you still have that as your basis because the change you experienced was only ignited by what you knew initially.

For example, let's say you were raised to believe your race was superior than every other race. As you grew older, you discovered the real inequalities that are presented in this world and you developed a growth mindset that reminded you one race is no better than any other. You began to pay more attention to racial inequalities, and that became a focus for your thoughts. Instead of continuing the belief that you are superior to others, you instead strive to think the opposite. Though you might have completely different ideas, that does not necessarily mean that you don't still have some similar thought patterns.

You might think more about racial inequalities than somebody who never considered this issue at all throughout their entire life. In this way, the trauma that we experience as children will also develop our mindsets. In some cases, severe trauma can limit your growth and keep you in the thinking pattern you had at the time that you experienced the trauma. When you are presented with triggers, those can also bring you back to the same kinds of feelings you had as a child. We'll talk about triggers in the next section, but right now, let's look at what childhood trauma you might have experienced.

Even seemingly normal households aren't always safe from traumatic experiences, especially if you attended a social school. Your family might have been picture-perfect, but that doesn't necessarily mean there weren't any horrific accidents or other tragedies which shaped the person that you are now. Let's look at some of the most obvious and common types of trauma that children experience.

The first one is physical abuse. This is very common among children, especially because it was widely and ignorantly accepted as a punishment for so long. Over 3 million cases of child abuse are investigated each year in the United States alone. This number represents the number of households, meaning that in actuality, more than 6 million children are exposed to these types of abusive situations.

Not every investigation warrants an actual charge, because there might be misunderstandings. At the same time, not every case of child abuse is actually reported or investigated in the first place.

We can assume that, with a report of child abuse being made every 10 seconds within just the United States, this is something still happening frequently. Emotional abuse is also common, and is even harder to prosecute because there isn't as much visible evidence. If somebody hits you, you have a bruise. If somebody hurts your feelings, however, it's not as easy to point out and show other people, especially for a child. Children don't know necessarily that they are being abused, because the person that is causing this pain is often the person responsible for teaching them about life.

Sexual abuse is also very common and can happen not just from parents, but from grandparents, aunts, uncles, older siblings, and anybody that children might be exposed to through daycare or schooling. Neglect is also a form of abuse that is often overlooked. You might think that because somebody is absent in your life, they can't be abusing you, but sometimes that restriction of visitation is the very thing which causes the abuse. Physical neglect is also something that could cause underlying trauma. Children might have learning disabilities, health conditions, or other problems that need treated by medical professionals, and yet they are able to get that care because of the household they are in. Physical neglect can also include not having proper nutrition. Many children will go without breakfast or dinner, because they are only fed what they are given at school. Children also simply need to be nurtured and played with. They need to be taught by their family. It shouldn't just be left up to schoolteachers to help develop a child, and yet many parents will simply expect the professionals to take the lead on their child's education. All of these forms of abuse can cause somebody to have struggles later in life.

It can be challenging to identify childhood trauma, because it doesn't always look the way we might expect. Unfortunately, it is very real, and can cause many children to face grave challenges. These struggles seem normal because it is all we know, but once you start to form a life as an adult, they can emerge in seemingly disconnected ways.

Knowing Your Triggers

When it comes to understanding how to manage your stress, it's important that we recognize what our triggers are. Your triggers are not things that are going to be specific to a symbol. For example, we often think of soldiers as individuals who struggle with PTSD as those who can be easily triggered. They might hear something that sounds like a gunshot which can put them back in the mindset they had at the moment that they experienced that trauma.

Symbolic triggers are very real. If you are in a car accident, you might struggle with cars. If you had a bad experience with clowns at a childhood birthday party, you might be triggered when you see somebody wearing such a costume.

These are things you are probably already aware of, in terms of what your triggers might be. Aside from these clear symbols, it's important that we recognize that these triggers provide us with feelings.

In order to recognize your triggers, you want to look at what these various symbols cause you to feel. Which emotion was evoked by a situation that you were in?

These feelings can be triggering and bring you back to the mindset you had at the moment the trauma occurred. But the thing that triggers those feelings might not be specifically related to your trauma.

For example, let's say that as a child, you were neglected by your mother and had been abandoned by your father. This could lead to feelings of abandonment later in your life. If you are broken up with unexpectedly when you are in love with somebody you thought would be around for a while, this might trigger you to have some of those same feelings. If a friend is not texting you back, you might wonder if they are neglecting you, and that can trigger those same kinds of feelings you experienced when you suffered the abuse from your mother. They're seemingly unconnected, but they can still take you to a place where you have those similar feelings.

That's not always so easily identifiable, which is why it will take some reflecting on your past to determine what might be triggering these emotions today.

Other triggering responses include feeling:

- lonely
- judged
- blamed
- excluded
- powerless
- unsafe
- unloved
- disconnected
- trapped
- manipulated
- controlled
- ignored
- uncared for
- disrespected

These might be feelings that were evoked in your childhood by peers or by the people that raised you, but they can also be feelings that you developed as an adult. If you were a child whose parents frequently belittled you and made you feel as though you were stupid, you might now feel ashamed when you don't understand a situation. Perhaps someone at work is trying to explain something to you and you struggle to take this educational moment and instead become defensive. Maybe you're afraid to speak up and ask for help, because when you did so as a child, a parent shamed you for not being very intelligent.

As an adult, you can still develop these triggers. Perhaps an ex-partner emotionally abused you and made you feel stupid for bringing up your feelings. They might have told you that you were crazy or being irrational. This can cause shame later, when you try bringing up your feelings with a new partner.

Reaction Versus Response

In the beginning steps of managing your emotions and your stress, it's important to ensure you recognize the difference between your reaction and your response.

How many times have you heard somebody say, "I couldn't help it, I was angry," or "I didn't mean to, I was sad," o "It's not my fault, I was upset?"

Emotions, and especially intense ones, make it more challenging for us to properly manage the way that we respond. But there is still a difference between the reaction you have and the response you choose to take.

Your reaction is automatic. It's the first thing that comes to you. It's your emotions that you feel that have been triggered by the situation. Your response, however, is the way that you choose to use that reaction. Your response is something deliberate. You're in control of it, and it is based on your thoughts and reflection of that emotion.

For example, let's say that you're really angry because a friend said something upsetting to you. Your reaction is that you feel hurt, and you're sad that this person thought this way about you. Your response is that you can either choose to talk it out and work through your issues, or you might decide to say something really mean back to them.

Another easy example that many of us have probably witnessed in our lives is how somebody might get worked up after losing a game. Maybe they're watching their favorite team playing in an important game, and their team blows it and loses the title in the last minute. They react with anger and are clearly upset. That's perfectly normal – it's actually healthy to be passionate about and emotionally invested in something.

However, this person may also respond by throwing their remote at the TV, punching a hole in the wall, or being mean to their family the rest of the day, simply because their team lost.

Reaction and response are two separate things. It is totally valid for you to have whichever reaction you have, but it is not healthy for you to respond in a way that you don't control. We all have power over our emotions and, as autonomous adults, it's important that we show this.

Chapter 2

Making Peace with Imperfection

We don't live in a perfect world, and the chances of running into someone who is actually perfect are pretty slim. Still, perfection becomes the main focus for many individuals all over the world. In every facet of life, there is pressure to be perfect.

You have to look perfect. You have to think perfectly. Everything you say has to be perfect. You have to have the perfect spouse. The perfect house. The perfect kids. The perfect job.

What we often overlook is just how boring perfection can be! Think back to any moment in your life that brings you joy. There is a good chance that this occurrence was one that was born from imperfection. Maybe it was the day you got caught in the rain with a friend. Maybe you bonded and laughed with family over the burnt turkey during the holidays.

Whatever these instances might be, it's essential we recognize just how much imperfection has helped us to become the people that we are today. If everyone was born looking and acting the same, how would we ever be able to form meaningful connections? If you never had to work to grow who you are from the inside out, what kind of person would you look like now?

The constant struggle to achieve higher and higher levels of perfection is exhausting. Where do these pressures come from? Why do we put such an emphasis on perfection, when we all know very well nothing in life is perfect? Everything is temporary, and it is often the flaws that show the true beauty of a situation. In this chapter, we're going to discuss why we feel so desperate to be perfect, and we'll help you better recognize the ways that you can begin to not only accept imperfection, but embrace it.

The Fake Pressures of Society

We all strive to do the best we can. But not everybody is going to be perfect, nor should they even want to be! How boring life would be if we were not flawed creatures.

Perfection is an idea created by other people. It puts pressure on us to be people that we aren't. Our society creates a lot of pressure that is put on each of us.

It's important that we recognize what these pressures are and how they shouldn't really matter to you at all. One of the reasons why society can put so much pressure on people is because of intrinsic capitalist ideologies.

For starters, the weight-loss industry is a huge source of stress for so many people. The pressure to have the perfect body, to diet as much as you can, to try out new fads, to have the best workout gear, the best clothes, and so on, all put so much pressure on people. Anytime you go to the store, you'll undoubtedly find a regular version of a specific food, as well as the "lite" version or the "fat-free" version or the "low-calorie" version. These are important things in some respects (like fat-free) because we do want to eat a healthy diet, but the emphasis is not always put on your health – instead, it's typically about your appearance.

The weight-loss industry is a $72-billion market.

At some point in your life, you have been convinced you were not good enough because somebody else was set to profit from these insecurities. Whether it's diet supplements, diet food, diet pills, diet lollipops, or anything else that helps you lose weight, these products are specifically marketed to 'fix' your insecurities. There are teams of marketers whose job it is to convince you to purchase the product so that you can fit into this idea of having the perfect body.

Another industry that puts pressure on people is the fashion industry. This is actually a $2.4-trillion market. If we all stopped caring about the way we looked and what we wore, people would be losing out on trillions of dollars. It's not okay for us to go through life *not* knowing this, because it will destroy our self-esteem.

Another industry that is highly expensive is the wedding industry. This is $53-billion industry, as well. Whether it's about securing the perfect venue, booking the best photographer, or wearing the best dress, this is a profitable market. It's a special day, of course, but it's just that – *one* day. Many couples still feel pressure to break the bank celebrating in the most fashionable way possible, all because the more you put into your wedding, the more you put into your love, right?

These things have lost all of their meaning. Clothes are no longer a way to express yourself, they are a way to highlight your status. The wedding industry is not about sharing love anymore, it's about showing other people how big this event can be. The weight loss industry isn't about health and nutrition, it's about looking good. These companies prey off of our insecurities, because we know that that is where we will put money. If you're not happy in your life, then you might put money towards one of these areas, because they promise happiness. Then, when you don't get that fulfillment, the search for happiness continues. These pressures can destroy us. They cause us immense pain, guilt, and shame. All of this can destroy our self-esteem if we are not aware of the way we are being tricked into buying things.

Understanding Self-Esteem

Social media is also a rising industry, with over $50 billion spent on ad revenue alone. These ads are used to target people who are already going to be looking at their social media feeds and feeling bad about themselves as they compare their lives to the lives of the people that they choose to follow. These industries are leeching off of our self-esteem.

Your self-esteem is a need that has to be fulfilled in order to provide you with a certain level of worth.

Having to feel safe and protected is the same as having to feel as though you are loved and wanted. If you go your entire life without having any self-esteem at all, it can cause loneliness, anxiety, and even depression. Your self-esteem is all about how much you love yourself and how secure you feel with who you are. When your self-esteem is too low, you'll be insecure, lacking confidence, and unable to have effective emotional control over your thoughts and feelings. If your self esteem is too high, you might have narcissistic tendencies, or it could be challenging for you to actually evaluate yourself in a healthy way.

There needs to be a balance.

It's good to love yourself and be confident, but it's also important to notice your flaws so that you can try to work on them. You need to have a level of self-actualization. You need to be aware of who you are, and you need to be able to express that and share that with other people. When that need goes unfulfilled, it makes us feel empty and lonely. Of course, everybody is going to have varying levels of self-esteem and not every person is going to be able to work on this as easily as some. What's important is that we notice it. When we are aware of our level of self-esteem, we can begin to form a solid foundation to grow those abilities.

Those with a healthy level of self-esteem are assertive and able to use their voice to share their needs with others. Those with the healthiest self-esteem will not be afraid of failure –

they know it's going to help them grow. They accept the person they are and they don't feel inferior or superior to other people. They're confident but not arrogant, they're able to take feedback and work and grow from this, they don't seek approval from other people but from themselves, instead. These are all things that you should begin to shoot for as you grow your self-esteem.

Adopting a Growth Mindset

You should strive to have a growth mindset over a fixed mindset. A growth mindset is one where you can focus on learning new things, self-reflecting for improvement, and changing your thoughts on a consistent basis. A fixed mindset is one where you're set in your ways and unwilling to change. When your mindset is fixed, you limit yourself and put too many labels and too much pressure on who you are as an individual.

With a growth mindset, you recognize that failure is the way that you can grow to become a better person. You're able to look at your challenges and let them become the motivation that pushes you to be greater. You are not afraid of feedback and you take everything that other people tell you in a way that helps improve who you are. You try new things and seek out new experiences so that you can constantly be growing. You are inspired by others and not afraid to have role models and people that you emulate.

A fixed mindset is one where you believe that one label defines who you are. You might have a moment in life where you don't succeed, and you let that become a label when you call yourself a loser. You might not think that you're good at anything at all, so you don't even bother to try. You don't like challenges because they cause you stress and fear. You don't do things because you simply don't think that you can. You're frustrated easily and you give up without trying. You don't take feedback well, and instead believe everybody who gives any sort of criticism is a villain who is out to get you. You believe that you already know everything, that you're intelligent and don't need to change.

The problem with a fixed mindset is that it's not going to help us improve at all. It's just going to keep us stuck in our ways, not advancing in a healthy manner. A fixed mindset is one that tells you that you are a specific type of person and that's all you're allowed to be. We have to move on from this, and instead focus on how we can let our brains really flourish.

Technique #1: Accept the Flaws of Life

The first tip we have for you is to accept the flaws of life. You have to get used to the reality that you will always have problems, issues, mistakes, accidents, regrets, and everything in between.

But that does not define who you are.

You aren't perfect, and you will likely never be. Other people might judge you, you might judge yourself. Things won't go as expected. There are going to be struggles in life.

Everything that seems bad needs to be accepted.

That might sound silly, or simple to some people, but it is quite complex when you think about it. We strive constantly to push out imperfections, as if they are abnormalities. We buy cream to get rid of our pimples, even though everybody has them. We fix our teeth with braces, even though people are rarely born with perfectly straight teeth. We crash diet even if we are healthy, because we think we need to be skinnier. We keep our doors shut and don't let people see our bedroom because of the dirty laundry in the corner, even though everybody has dirty laundry in their room. We hide our burps and our farts, even though everybody burps and farts. We're ashamed about going to the bathroom, even though everybody does it.

This isn't to say that it should be widely accepted to just let your gas out whenever and wherever. Common courtesy is nice, but it shouldn't be such an embarrassment when you let one slip.

We hide our imperfections as if they are not normal. That, in itself, is abnormal. Everybody has their flaws, and if we lived in a society where we embraced and celebrated these things rather than shutting them out as if they didn't exist, we'd have a lot more healthy people.

This method is really just about accepting the fact that we are always going to have things we wish we could improve.

Notice your own flaws. Recognize these as things that make you the individual you are.

Next, pick out flaws that you might see in other people, and recognize the way that these flaws actually make them who they are. You might have a friend who has freckles. These are likely imperfections to her, but to you, they might be charming and cute.

A friend might have a lisp that they're insecure about, but in your opinion, this is something endearing.

Other people's flaws might not be as charming in every situation, but that doesn't mean that they need to be rejected completely. We have to learn to take the bad with the good.

Not everything is going to be as it seems. If we continue to strive, to accept, and to embrace, we can focus on what matters most.

Chapter 3

Taking Control of the Controllable

People often lose control and stress about things they don't have power over. This can lead to heart attacks and other stress-related issues down the line. In this chapter, we are going to discuss things in the present, letting go of the factors that are outside of our control.

The only thing that we have control over is this moment. What happened in the past is done. What will happen in the future cannot be predicted. Even if you are able to see ahead to everything that might happen, there will always be a certain level of unpredictability that we will have to accept.

The only thing that is certain is that everything is uncertain.

You can be the most prepared and ready individual on the planet, but you will still have difficulty accepting the randomness of life if you are not focused on embracing chance and unpredictability.

It is sometimes the individuals who are so prepared who have the biggest difficulty dealing with random occurrences. Those that "go with the flow" may not be as prepared, but they can usually adjust better when something doesn't go as expected.

Aside from the attention we give to the future, we also have to recognize how much we can live in the past. You might experience constant regret and moments of guilt, but there can also be one singular moment that we end up ruminating over. It's never easy to hold onto so much desire and wish for change. Rather than looking at ways to make the most of the future, many will struggle with what they've done and will relive these scenarios over and over again in their head.

It's time to embrace the moments that are surrounding us now. Mistakes are a part of life, and they help create the people that we are. There are many resulting effects that can come from just a simple accident, so we can't be forever angry that we didn't try harder. The "could haves" of life will always be there, so rather than trying to live perfectly and avoid this, we have to learn how to embrace these factors.

Dealing with Regret and Guilt

Regret and guilt are things that can eat away at you. Even if it causes constant stress, headaches, stomach pain, back pain, clenched jaws, and so on, you might still struggle to let go of the past.

Emotions like regret and guilt are so hard because they are out of our control. Clearly, the best answer to address that regret or guilt is to go back in time and fix whatever went wrong. Unfortunately, we have not yet uncovered a way to travel through time, so for now, we have to come up with alternative ways to fix those feelings of regret, remorse, and guilt that can consume our minds.

It's not just about regret over what you did to somebody else – it might be guilt you put on yourself. Perhaps you flunked out of college, maybe you didn't take that job across the country. It could be that you broke up with somebody you feel like you should have married.

Whatever these life events might be, they could be the very things that are keeping you trapped in a mentality of feeling regretful over your past mistakes. These things are out of our control because very infrequently is there an actual way to remedy the situation. If you have hurt somebody, you can sometimes make up for this regret or remorse by apologizing to them and making amends. But not everybody might be ready to accept your apologies, either – sometimes, you're just going to have to sit with your guilt.

There are a few things you can do to begin to take back control over these challenging emotions. First, accept the fact that it happened. Sometimes, we still have so much regret because we are in a mentality where that situation has become the reality. Maybe you lost a friend who passed away from suicide. Any form of death can make us feel guilty, but when somebody takes their own life, it's hard not to blame yourself.

Maybe you could have called them more. Maybe you should have sent them a letter. Maybe you should have been hanging out with them the night they died. Sometimes, this guilt is there because you haven't yet accepted the reality of the situation.

The reality of something like suicide is that it is nobody else's fault. That person had a psychological condition that manifested from other reasons, and ultimately, they made a decision. While it might have been influenced by various events, and perhaps they could have been saved, it's still nobody else's fault – we just have to accept that as reality. Even if you triggered them and ignited the situation, you still cannot be blamed. Think of others who were in the same situaiton who didn't commit suicide. As tragic as something like this is, it is nobody's fault, not even the person who took their life.

The next thing you can do is look at what value has come from your guilt. Has this decade of regret really made up for the event that occurred so many years ago? Are you actually helping the person you might feel regret or remorse over? Is this guilt creating a stronger and better person?

Recognize the trigger of these guilty thoughts and stop them as they're happening. Envision yourself as the person that you might feel regret over. For example, maybe you bullied somebody or even were emotionally abusive to another person at some point in your life. You should make amends to them and let them know that you understand what you did was wrong, because it could help them in their healing process. After that, if you still have guilt, imagine how they would feel if the roles were reversed.

Would that guilt really make you feel better? Would it make you feel good to know that somebody else is suffering, even if they hurt you? There's no point in both people being miserable. Everybody should be doing their best to heal and move on, to find growth from the situation rather than ruminating in the same emotions, over and over again.

Remember that guilt is natural, and it can teach us something. Maybe you did lose a loved one and you feel guilty for not spending enough time with them.

Of course, we will always, always, always have that feeling. There is never enough time in one lifetime to spend with people that you love the most.

Just one more hug. Just one more kiss. Just one more, "Hey, thanks for being a friend." We will always have that regret, and something like that is hard to deal with. But it does remind us to appreciate the people that are still here even more.

You can use your guilt to grow, but don't let it become something that completely destroys you. It's all about balance.

Anxiety and Panic

Anxiety and panic are emotional states that stem from situations that are usually out of our control. Anxiety can come from fear over the future or regret over the past. We've already talked about the past, so let's focus on how you might carry worry over the things that lie ahead.

The thing about panic is that it can come from a feeling of being overwhelmed. Panic attacks can be triggered by many different situations, but they can also come out of nowhere if you have chronic and unmanaged anxiety. One of the reasons it is so overwhelming is because there are so many options as to what might happen in the future.

Even going to work tomorrow, things could take a really crazy turn. Though they may be unexpected, not all potential scenarios are negative. However, our minds can gravitate towards more negative thoughts. You might show up to work and learn your boss was fired, or died, or quit, and now you have a new boss. Maybe the building burned down, maybe the building is getting renovated. Maybe the building got broken into. Maybe a war breaks out in your country. Maybe you wake up and you feel sick and you have to call off work. Maybe you get in a car accident on the way there.

All of these things are negative things that could happen. They come naturally to us because our brains are going to go towards the worst. Maybe tomorrow you find a $100 bill on the ground. Maybe you run into a friend you haven't seen in a while and you rekindle that relationship. Maybe you get a promotion – maybe everybody gets a promotion! Maybe your office is getting a makeover.

Anything could happen.

And all these thoughts swirl in our minds, but most of the time, those with anxiety will have a negative view of how things could go. When you have all of those potentials, it can be extremely overwhelming and cause you panic. These worries and stress are natural and normal, and it's not always a bad thing.

While you should be prepared, you don't want to be that kind of Doomsday-paranoid individual, because that can really eat away at the time you do have.

Think about any one of these things could happen, and remind yourself that the worry you have now is not going to change that. Tomorrow, maybe a building does burn down. The only thing you can do to be prepared for that is to make sure that you're safe. You have no power over what your neighbors do, unfortunately, so they may be the cause of that, which would be out of your control. You also have to recognize the way that you might have difficulty, even being prepared for these negative situations.

Adesh Silva

All you can do is your best to be ready. Worrying is never going to stop that situation from happening. You should acknowledge that you could lose your job, but obsessing over getting fired will make you sick to the point it might affect your work. You should acknowledge that we can lose loved ones at any moment, but if you are constantly afraid of death, it will eat away at your time alive.

When you have this worry over the future, take a look at your past. When has being nervous or paranoid ever helped you? In some ways, maybe it has. Perhaps you go out and you buy a more expensive renter's insurance to protect your items after being paranoid about an apartment fire. Perhaps you keep backup supplies in your car for any emergencies after having your car break down in the past. These things are normal and healthy.

However, when you constantly have that worried mentality, it's not going to do any good – and it's certainly not going to prevent bad things from happening.

Technique #2: Understand What You Have Power Over

Take Control Of Your Day

It's essential that we let go of our need for *total* control. Remove yourself from the mentality where you have to have power over everything. One of the reasons we like to have control is because we are afraid of what might happen. We get this idea that if you do have power over people or power over events, then bad things can't happen.

When you're sort of free falling, you might not know where you will land, and that can be really terrifying. Humans have the natural desire to have power. This doesn't mean that they want to be the dictator of the country. It simply means we have this urge to have a certain level of control over our lives and our situation. It's a survival skill. If you only depend on other people, when it comes down to it, they're going to be looking out for themselves first – you might not get all of your needs met. This kind of control is important for us to maintain, but not in an extreme way. This is when people can become power hungry. They might be controlling over a situation and think that they know best, even though they may not. It's time to let go of some of that need for power and move on.

The first thing you want to do is make sure you let yourself trust other people. It's okay if they might not do it as perfectly as you can, but we still have to give everybody else the chance to try. Make sure you keep yourself in this moment and ask why you need to have that control. For example, if you have abandonment issues, then you might control other people because you're afraid they're going to leave you. If you are fearful over losing your job, you might be controlling in a managerial position because you're afraid that other people are going to be the reason that you lose your job. Ask yourself why you need to have this power and where it is coming from and it will tell you a lot about yourself.

Technique #3: Practice Mindfulness

Mindfulness is the act of being grounded in this moment. It's something we all should be practicing on a daily basis. Too often, we give our time to the future or let it be stuck in the past. Rather than enjoying this moment, you might be afraid of what's going to happen tomorrow, or the day after and the day after that.

Consider the last time you were hanging out with friends but were too anxious over what they might be thinking, or what might happen next, for you to actually enjoy the moment. Sometimes, you might even struggle with memory, because you've spent too much time in a different place rather than listening and enjoying and embracing everything that existed around you.

Mindfulness is going to pull you from those other moments and bring you right into this one. The first tip from mindfulness is to simply sit in a comfortable place and notice your surroundings. Pick out one color and identify everything in the room that is that particular color.

For example, you might choose red. Maybe you notice the red pillow sitting on the bed. Perhaps there's a red painting on the wall. Maybe the red on the alarm clock is visible. That's it. All you have to do is notice your surroundings, and you'll be brought back into this moment.

You might go straight back into anxious thoughts, but then you would just repeat the activity with a different color. Pick out everything that's blue. Maybe the curtain is blue, the carpet is blue, the pillow is blue. Continue this until you are pulled from those anxious thoughts and able to focus on the present. The more that you do this, the easier it will be to think clearly about the things that are giving you anxiety, rather than letting them fester and build panic in your mind.

Another activity of mindfulness is to notice one thing that you can identify with your senses. This means noticing one thing you can touch. One thing you can taste. One thing you can smell. One thing you can hear, and one thing you can see. Work your way through the senses, and you'll be able to pull yourself back into the present.

Chapter 4

Exercise and the Effects on You

Stress often seems like something that is completely mental. How many times have you heard people tell you, "It's all in your head," "Just relax," "Stop freaking out," and so on. These statements seem so easy, because you can alter your brain quicker than your body. You can decide you want to do something that, moments ago, you were against. It's not as easily done as it is to say, but we still have to remember that changing your mind is easier than switching around the chemical processes in your body.

That being said, stress is not all mental. Your physical anatomy is going to play directly into the way that your mind works. We are one giant entity, after all, not just a separation of all systems. Though our nervous, skeletal, muscular, digestive, and other systems operate in their own ways, it is the team working together that makes us who we are. The things that you put in your body, as well as the exercises that it endures, will play directly into how your mind operates, overall.

Exercising every day can help you reduce stress on your body. It can get your mind moving and your blood pumping. It can help you focus better and relieve tension. It is a way to better enable yourself to maintain your health. Not only is exercise important, but what you eat will greatly alter your mind, too. You might struggle with energy levels or have brain fog because of the things you choose to put in your body.

This chapter is dedicated to the physical side of health. It's not about dieting or getting the most expensive gym membership, either. We're not here to tell you to lose weight or start muscle training. It doesn't matter if you're a size 0 or a size 20. Everyone needs to move their body, and everyone needs to make sure they are balancing their diet between healthy foods and foods that make them feel good mentally.

Don't feel pressured to completely change your lifestyle, as this is not a fitness book meant to help you "shed pounds." It's all about how nutrition plays into your mental health — an aspect of weight regulation that is too frequently overlooked. Eating healthy and exercising isn't exclusive to appearance. It's all about how we treat our bodies that will affect how they feel, inside and out.

How Your Health Affects Your Mind

Our minds are clearly the most complex organisms in our bodies. What we overlook as being almost as complex is our stomachs. Your stomach is actually a microbiome, which means that inside of it are millions of bacteria, working to make sure that you have proper digestion. In this microbiome exists microflora, which is responsible for the production of serotonin. In fact, about 95% of the serotonin in your body is produced within your gastrointestinal tract. What this means is that the foods you eat are going to affect serotonin produced within your body.

When you're eating like garbage, then you're going to feel like garbage. That good bacteria in your stomach is important for breaking down food, but also for producing hormones. When you're not helping that to flourish, you'll end up struggling with your mental health. In fact, studies have shown those who eat a more traditional diets, such as the Japanese diet or a Mediterranean diet, have a much lower chance of being diagnosed with depression.

Sometimes, it can be as simple as changing our diet, which can help drastically reduce our stress. If you're always eating unhealthy and never exercising, then it would be surprising if you weren't struggling with stress, honestly. Do your best to notice the things that you're eating and start making healthier choices. We will discuss what is good and what is bad for your diet at the end of this chapter.

Why Exercise is Important

One of the most obvious signs of the positive effects of exercise is that it helps you balance your weight and boost your self-esteem. If you have a fit body, then you might have fewer struggles with your bodily appearance. Of course, that's not to say that those who work out are more attractive than others. It's just that when you put that effort towards your body, it can help elevate your level of self-esteem. Exercise also helps maintain a certain level of muscle strength in your body, which will increase your endurance, as well as your overall energy levels.

If you're constantly lethargic and always tired, it can be harder to manage your stress. Exercising releases endorphins and helps regulate hormones, which means it may also improve your mood. If you're not exercising enough, then you're not using up your body's energy sources and those can be depleted, or stored as fat. It's important that we burn these calories within our body not just to fit into a bikini or our favorite dress, but because it helps to regulate every other part of your overall health. Exercise is also important because it helps make sure that your sleep is maintained. If you don't get enough exercise throughout the day, you may find you are restless at night.

We are animals, and just like how a dog needs to get outside to go for a walk, we need to make sure that we use that kind of physical strength in our lives to boost our moods. Exercise can also be a social activity. It might not even be about the actual act of exercise, but rather how you are doing it, which can make you feel better – going to dance classes with friends, taking self-defense lessons to make you feel more secure, and getting a gym membership and interacting with people you meet there can be a great way to boost your self-esteem. Always look for the health benefits of exercise aside from losing weight, because that's just a stigma attached that we need to get over. It can cause a mentality where if you don't want to lose weight, then you don't really care about exercising.

Technique #4: Get Active

Whatever you do, just get more active. The recommended amount of exercise per day is 30 minutes. This means that you should be exercising for three and a half hours every week. If you can't do 30 minutes a day, that's fine. Do an hour and 15 minutes on three different days. Do really long sessions at the gym. Whatever you need to do to get your body moving, do it.

The hard part about managing stress and exercising is that a lot of individuals who might struggle with anxiety are going to struggle with exercising, because that act alone might trigger them to state of anxiousness. For example, perhaps you have social anxiety because you're insecure about your appearance, as you've been overweight since you were a child.

Maybe you struggled in gym class because you weren't the best athlete, and now the thought of exercising or even stepping foot into a gym makes you panic. That is okay, and perfectly normal.

What we have to do then is look for other ways of exercising. You don't have to go the traditional route of working out over and over again on the same machine. The most common way to exercise is to simply go for walks. Find nature trails in your area, take a different route to work and walk home, skip the bus, skip the train and go on foot. A 30-minute walk every day can really be enough to boost those good feelings inside of you and make it so that you can better manage your mental health. Hiking is also a great activity and gets you out in nature. You can do these kinds of activities with your friends, making it easier to stay connected and be social with others that will encourage and hold you accountable.

Dancing is another great way to get moving, as well taking a self-defense classes. These have added benefits besides just working you out. You can protect yourself if you know how to fight back in an attack, or you can impress people with your dance moves when you go out to the clubs.

Look for small methods to incorporate more movement, as well. Maybe you could get a standing desk or an exercise ball for when you're at work all day. Park farther away at the grocery store so you have to walk. Carry weights around with you as you're walking around to the house. Some things might make you feel a little uncomfortable, but does that really matter when you're taking care of your health?

Technique #5: Eat the Right Food

It's important that we begin to watch what we eat, because it can be impacting your body. The first thing you should be trying to limit is processed and highly sugary foods. Aside from just the immense level of sodium or sugar that might be found at things like chips, candy, soda, crackers, and so on, they also have additives.

These additives are put in to make them taste better, last longer, or have a certain color. Since they are in small amounts, they seem harmless on a per-snack basis. But if all you are eating is highly processed food, then you're overloading your body, and that can be negatively impacting the microflora that exists within your stomach.

Additives aren't just found in the seemingly unhealthy foods, either. Foods like diet soda can have artificial sweeteners which could impact your overall cognitive function.

Not only do these kinds of additives affect the function of your body, they can also cause inflammation. Inflammation is the body's attack against any outside intrusion or infection. Think of the last time that you got a little scrape. Your skin will become red and swollen, trying to fight that infection out.

If you are putting things in your body that are too difficult to be properly broken down, it could lead to inflammation. The inflammation occurs in your brain, or in your joints, or in your muscles. It might cause you to be sore, tired, depressed, and cranky.

What you can do to prevent this is to make sure that you eat more antioxidant-rich foods. These are going to be fruits and veggies that are dark and vibrant in color. Think of things like spinach or kale, purple cabbage, berries, pomegranates, and so on. These are full of antioxidants that can fight off that inflammation.

Alcohol is also something that can cause intense inflammation. However, if you choose a glass of red wine, that small amount could actually help reduce some inflammation. It's all about moderation.

Nuts and seeds, as well as omega-three fatty acid fish, can be another great source of probiotics, which can help balance your stomach. Citrusy or acidic foods like tomatoes and oranges, as well as lemons, can also produce some of that anti-inflammation needed in the body.

Green tea and coffee are great additions, as well. Whatever you do, try to maintain a level of health in your life. When you do indulge in some fast food, a night of drinking, or a sugary midnight snack, don't shame yourself, because we also need to have some fun with these foods.

If you deprive yourself of the things that you're used to eating and the things you like, that might help your body, but it's not going to be great for your mind, because you'll be craving that. This could be stressful, especially if you do something like crash dieting or unplanned fasting.

Let yourself have these moments where you indulge, but don't let it be a normal thing. Don't eat fast food every day, but if you eat fast food once every other week, then that's not going to cause stress directly. When you do eat these foods that might be processed, just combat them. Maybe you do want to have some nice cheese and bacon. Rather than eating a big bacon cheeseburger, what about a chicken bacon ranch salad with plenty of onions, spinach, and tomatoes?

Perhaps you are looking forward to a night of pizza and beer. Order a side of veggies with that, and just eat one less slice of pizza.

It's not about all or nothing. You can find that balance, and that's what's more important than trying to have a super restrictive diet which causes you even more stress.

Chapter 5

The Power of Self-Talk

You are in your head more than anyone else ever will be. Even if someone is actively trying to control your mind, you will still get the last word in! Unfortunately, far too many people don't talk to themselves in a healthy way. It's almost as if that self-doubt and inner bully is more natural than an internal voice that is compassionate and caring.

It's taken a while to develop the voice that is inside of us. It is a combination of the people who raised us, the friends we surround ourselves with, the shows and movies we choose to watch, the books we've read, the lessons we've learned, and everything in between. It is your voice, but it is also inspired by the things that other people have helped ignite within you.

Sometimes, it's almost as if there are two, or even three voices in our head. It's not necessarily that there are "voices," like we are hearing things that aren't really there. It's simply a battle between the various thoughts that we may have. You probably have some self-doubt. A voice in your head tells you, "just do it," but then another one says, "well, have you actually thought about…"

You might have a voice in your head that tells you "you look great tonight!" but then another one interrupts by saying, "except for that pimple on your chin." When it comes to managing self-talk, we have to know what these different voices are and where they came from. Were they planted there by someone else? Did you develop them simply from society? What has been your biggest struggle in overcoming these constant thoughts? The more you can reflect and dive deep into that voice inside of you, the easier it will be to manage it properly.

Looking at the Root

When it comes to identifying why you might be saying the things that you are to yourself, it's important that we begin to look at the root of where these thoughts came from. Most of the time, these are reactions to lowered self-esteem, and that can really cause some negative side effects if we're not careful. You want to first look where these thoughts developed, so that you can know exactly how to fight them off.

The first reason that you might have these thoughts is the simple pattern of repetition. You might have consistently believed these things throughout your life. For example, you might have been told by your parents that you were not good enough as a child. As you grow into an adult, you still continually tell yourself that you aren't good enough, over and over again. This can cause some serious damage to your self-esteem, and it can be hard to turn those views around.

You might also just be around negative people, or in a negative space that promotes that kind of thinking as normal. It might be that you are comparing yourself to other people and seeking out their approval. When you are constantly doing things just for others, then you lose yourself in the process. If you only make art to impress people, then you're not going to actually enjoy creating art – it's going to be stressful and you're going to be worried about whether or not somebody else is actually going to like it. You might be comparing yourself to others in an unhealthy way, because you're not fully recognizing that other people have their own flaws.

For example, anytime you get on social media, you'll be able to find plenty of happy families, excited couples, and people that generally look like they're having a really good time. If you really dug deep and looked at their life, they likely have just as many issues as you, but they aren't going to show those on social media. They're not going to post those pictures of them with baby puke on them, or fighting with their husbands in the grocery store, and so on. They're just going to be sharing the good times, and that can create a false perspective if it's all we allow ourselves to see.

There might be some feelings of guilt and regret that are still coming up and causing you to feel a certain way. If you truly want to stop the negative self-talk from growing, then you have to pluck it from the root. You don't want to just shut these thoughts out of your head, because they're still going to be there, and they'll grow and fester in your brain. You want to take them out by the place that they have grabbed onto so hard.

How Others View You

Self-talk is hard because often, we're judging ourselves harder than any other person ever has. You have to recognize this and stop yourself from letting your beliefs be influenced by how other people might view you. Everybody has their own perspective. All of our experiences have created the people that we are now. Even if you could be exactly the person that you want to be, other people will still view you differently. No matter how hard you try to control somebody else's perspective, they will still be the one in charge, at the end of the day.

First and foremost, other people will view you based on what they might find more attractive. Some people might just prefer blondes, but you're brunette. Others might think eyes are more beautiful, whereas others prefer plumper lips. These preferences are going to determine how they might perceive you. Even if you were the perfect image for one person, you might be the exact opposite of what somebody else finds desirable.

Even the most beautiful person in the world probably still has some harsh critics. Beauty is so incredibly subjective and we have to stop trying to fit everyone into the same mold, because it will be our flaws at the end of the day that help us stick out to other people.

You have to remember that anybody who's judging you super harshly is also judging themselves, just as deep. Imagine how they must be talking about themselves when nobody else is around.

Your perspective is not going to be the same as that of the rest of the world, even after you get into a place where you have a high level of self-esteem. We can't let this disrupt our thoughts, though. You have to embrace that you are the person who you are, and all that really matters is how you see yourself. At the end of the day, it's going to be you looking back in the mirror, and nobody else, so you have to like what you see.

Technique #6: Breathe It Out

One thing that we have to do when we are getting super judgmental is first simply breathe. It's not always about what thoughts you can use to alter perspectives, what activities to participate in, or beginning other exercises for quieting your brain right off the bat. The first thing you have to do is simply focus on your breathing. To do this, start by sitting in a comfortable place. Keep your body stretched out and don't have any tension or anything restricting the way that you sit. Breathe in through your nose for five seconds, and out through your nose for five seconds. Breathe in as you count up, and then count back down.

By counting as you breathe, you help to focus your thoughts to one singular place. If you pair this technique with mindfulness, you'll be able to stop those negative thoughts. It can also help you feel better physically. We don't always realize that we are carrying physical stress in the moment, that our muscles might be tense and our heart is beating really fast. Breathe in and out, and you'll be able to regulate your body better.

Another good focused breathing activity is to breathe in through your nose as you count to five, and then breathe out through your nose in a really sharp and fast big breath out. This is sort of like dumping garbage. It's like cleaning yourself out, quickly getting rid of all that nastiness that's inside of your brain and those negative thoughts that are tearing you apart. It's like that one big breath out helps spill all of the garbage at once.

You can also try a popular form of yoga breathing. What you do is hold your hand out and make a fist, then stick your pinky and your thumb out. Place your right pinky on your left nostril and breathe in for five, then swap this position and place your thumb on your right nostril and breathe out for five. Continue to do this to help you be more focused and relaxed.

The final breathing exercise for you to try is breathing in through your nose and out through your mouth. You can breathe in for 10 and swallow, then breathe out for 10. If you do this for a couple minutes, you'll notice that you actually feel almost a high. It's as if your body is becoming relaxed and calm to the point that you took some sort of anti-anxiety medication. It's a really great way to focus your body and make sure that you are actually present in the moment.

Technique #7: Challenge Your Thoughts

When it comes to negative self-talk, it's important that we always challenge our thoughts. Challenging your thoughts means that denying that they are the truth. If you look in the mirror and think that you're ugly, sometimes, you'll believe this. The more that you repeat it to yourself, the easier it becomes to believe. Do not let yourself constantly think that these negative things are true.

The first thing to do to challenge your thoughts is to look for the evidence. When you say that you are ugly, ask, "Who said this?"

Did a doctor of ugliness determine this was the truth? Did the president of The Ugly Association just try to induct you?

There is usually no factual evidence to back this up. You might use other people's opinions as a way to validate your perspective, but those are opinions and not facts. It is not the truth.

After this, look at what evidence there is that combats this idea. For example, somebody telling you that you're beautiful is the exact evidence against this negative thought that you had. If you don't feel intelligent but somebody else called you smart, then that is proof that other people believe that you're smart. Too often, we ignore the good comments and just focus on the negative things people might have said. If you can't find any evidence for or against your perspective, then ask yourself if this is a perspective that somebody else could have differently.

Maybe you think that you are unattractive, and while you don't have any evidence against that, you also don't have any evidence telling you otherwise. However, perhaps you have gotten hit on when you went out to a bar recently, or you have several messages on a dating app.

That alone should tell you that even though nobody directly called you beautiful, other people do have the perspective that you are attractive. You can also challenge these thoughts by speaking to yourself as if you were talking to your best friend. If they were sitting across from you saying, "I'm so ugly, I'm so stupid nobody likes me," what would you say to make them feel better?

If you start to talk to yourself like this, it becomes easier to get into a more positive mindset. If you wouldn't feel comfortable saying negative things to a friend, then why is it okay for you to say this to yourself? What have you done in your life that really makes you think you believe such toxicity is punishment for you?

Continue to challenge your thoughts whenever they challenge you.

Chapter 6

How to Take Control of Your Mindset

Of all the things you can control in the world, your mindset is the only one that you have total power over. Unfortunately, not enough people realize this and instead will go through life with the belief that they are powerless over their thoughts and emotions. There was even a time when it was believed that once we reached the age of 30, our brains stopped developing and weren't able to be altered anymore.

This isn't the case at all! You are never too old to change your mindset. It's certainly easier when you're younger, but that doesn't mean it will ever be impossible. We will always have the power to change our minds. It isn't something that changes like a light switch, however. It is all about perspective and the way we have been taught to view the world. Your brain is entirely unique. Even if you had an identical twin, the way that you see the world would still be at least a little different.

This means your process of change is also going to be different from everyone else's. You might have no problem allowing positivity into your mindset, but you could also be so used to pessimism that it feels nearly impossible. What we have to remember, above all else, is that this process is one in which patience is key. It will take time to break old habits.

The first thought that you have about anything is usually what has been taught to you. It is the thoughts that follow after that are the most important. You might not be able to easily change that first thought, but afterwards, you can begin to alter your mind in a more positive and productive method. For example, if a girl walked into the room wearing a not-so-flattering dress, your first thought might be, "Why is she wearing that?" But what matters the most is what you think next. You might question yourself and ask, "Why does it matter what she wears?" You might say things like, "At least she's confident," or "She's beautiful the way she is." What matters most is that you are starting to form those more positive thoughts so that your brain can get into a pattern of change.

The Brain's Plasticity

Whenever you learn something new, it creates brand-new synapses in your brain. This is the formation of two neurons. The better you learn and remember this new information, the stronger that synapse is going to be. This is why it's important to study. You might learn that one plus one equals two, but if you only learn that once in your life, then you might forget it eventually. The more you practice something, the stronger that synapse is going to be, which means the easier it will be for you to remember and understand that important information when you need it later on.

Your brain has a certain level of neuroplasticity. What this refers to is the brain's ability to rearrange itself and function in a new way.

Neurogenesis is when you have consistent generation of neurons within a specified part of your brain. If you are constantly learning about the same subject, that means you're going to be continually creating new synapses in that area. New synapses are formed when you have a brand-new neural connections from information that wasn't known previously. Then, you can strengthen the synapses, which is done in neurogenesis as well. The repetition will make these even stronger, so that it's harder for them to break. The more you remember something, the harder it will be to forget about it.

Weakened synapses are those that are forgotten about. It's when you learn information and then you never go back to it. We have to remember that our brain can be constantly shaped and formed.

However, just as easily, it can be destroyed when we ignore it and overlook some of the benefits of increasing that neural plasticity. It's up to you to make sure you recognize your ability to strengthen your brain. You can make your brain stronger in an area that you already have knowledge of, or you can create a brand-new mindset around information that you're about to learn. All that really matters is that you are doing your best to increase these neural connections.

It's never too late for you to learn, and your brain is not too weak. You might need more practice than other people, but eventually, we'll be able to strengthen those connections.

Technique #8: Use Positive Affirmations

One thing that you can do to increase your brain strength is to use positive affirmations. Positive affirmations are verbal statements that enforce an idea that you already have.

For example, "I am strong" is an affirmation. It's as simple as that. Too often, we are repeating negative affirmations to ourselves without even realizing it. These might be things like "I'm not good enough," "I'm stupid," "I'm ugly," "I'm wrong," "I'm bad," "I deserve punishment," "I don't deserve anything good," "I am weak," "I am sad," or "I am a loser."

All of these are negative affirmations, but we don't always realize this. Sometimes, they just feel like natural thoughts.

The more you tell yourself that you're not worthy, you're unlovable, or that you're weak, the more you are going to believe it. These affirmations are also going to be strengthened by other people who say the same thing. If you have anyone in your life who does reinforce these negative affirmations, you should be doing your best to cut them out.

However, you won't always be able to shut these people out, so it's good to also make sure you're using positive affirmations to alleviate some of that belief. Outside of these simple negative affirmations, we can use other forms of evidence to validate those beliefs. For example, if you say to yourself that you are ugly all the time, that is a strong connection in your brain already present. If somebody else makes an off-hand comment that can kind of relate to your appearance, you might use that to validate that negative affirmation, making that synapse stronger. Maybe you get stood up for a date. They might not say anything at all about your appearance and the reason could be completely unrelated, but you might still use that to affirm this belief you already have. The more you use positive affirmations, the stronger those are going to be repeated in your head – the stronger those synapses are going to be, and the easier it will be for you to actually believe these things that you're telling yourself.

Positive affirmations include things like:

- I am brave.

- I am good.

- I am worthy.

- I am strong.

Whatever you do, look for ways to incorporate these affirmations. You can use them during breathing exercises, as well.

Repeat an affirmation. Breathe in, then breathe out.

You can also have physical reminders of these affirmations. You could carry a token with you. Maybe it's a lucky penny or a small stone in your pocket. Say affirmations as you hold this and then keep it with you. Whenever you are feeling insecure or like you are not strong enough to move forward, then you can touch this and get a reminder of just how worthy you really are. You can also write these affirmations down. The more you write them out, the more you will be able to strengthen them in your brain. When we write things down, it becomes easier to believe them. You could also write them down on signs and post them around your walls. Put an affirmation that says, "I am beautiful" on your mirror, so when you wake up in the morning, you remember to say that to yourself. The more you use affirmations, the stronger you will grow your brain in a direction that helps alleviate that anxiety and bring in peace.

Technique #9: Write and Journal

Journaling is going to be one of the most important things on your path to brain quietness. You'll want to get a journal as soon as possible so that you can begin to share your thoughts and your feelings. A journal helps you express things that you might not even be able to put into words just yet.

Start by choosing your medium. You can go out and purchase a lined notebook. You might have a journal already, or you can simply use the notes app on your phone. You can have a separate Word document on your desktop and go to it whenever needed and add journal entries. It autosaves and then you'll always have a copy that you can email to yourself, as well.

Start by journaling for at least five minutes a day. Set a timer on your phone and pick a specific time to just sit down and write. Write non-stop for the full five minutes. Just let your thoughts spill out, then you can start to include more prompts. There are many self-discovery prompts online that you can find which can help you have a basis for what to write about. These are things like, "What is your biggest dream?" "What is your biggest fear?" "Where do you see yourself in five years?" and so on.

The more you journal, the easier it's going to be for you to write your thoughts and feelings down. Often, we might have these sorts of emotions that we don't fully understand, and that can make things rather confusing. When you can flesh out these ideas and these beliefs, then you'll be able to put them into words. It will be easier to reflect on them and look back at the root of where some of these feelings might be coming from.

You also don't always have to journal in a creative way. Sometimes, it can be more analytical. Maybe you take down statistics of how you're feeling for the day. You could create a chart and notice your emotions at three different times of the day. You can go back and look at these statistics to determine what it might be that could be causing or triggering them, and get to the root of your problem.

Of course, if you can do both, by all means do that. You simply need a creative outlet where you can talk your thoughts out. You want to be able to make self-reflection as easy as possible so that it becomes more natural to do this on a consistent basis.

Chapter 7

Not Letting Your Emotions Dictate Your Life

Our emotions can make us feel like we have no control. Who hasn't been so angry they said something they didn't mean? So sad they did something they shouldn't have? So bored they made a silly mistake? Our emotions are what drive us, and sometimes, it's easy to let the wheel go a little wild while in the driver's seat. If you're not carefully checking in with your emotions and paying attention to what lies ahead, then you are going to let your emotions get the best of you.

It's essential that we start to check in with the way that we are thinking and feeling now. The thoughts and emotions you have aren't ones that you have to let destroy you! We can all live a perfectly happy and healthy life when we just get our emotions under control. There are a few things in this chapter we will go over so that you can stop being a victim of your emotions and instead take the lead for yourself.

83

Remember, no one else makes you feel the way that you do. Others might influence or trigger thoughts that lead to certain emotions, but at the end of the day, it is always going to be you that has the most control. It will always be within your range to be able to regulate the feelings that you have. Even when someone is intentionally making you angry, it is you that gets to decide whether this is something that will destroy you or make you stronger. Some might test your emotions and cause difficult feelings, but you always get to decide who is in charge.

Emotional Intelligence

Centering yourself around emotional intelligence is the way that you will be able to follow a path towards a more emotionally strong life. You want to be the Einstein of the things that you feel, so it's essential that we come up with a plan to make sure we are doing our best to maintain a high level of emotional intelligence. There are five different aspects of emotional intelligence that you will want to work on.

The first is self-awareness. This is when you can become knowledgeable of the mental state you are in and what that means. When you have self-awareness, you can look at how you feel and determine where that came from. Being self-aware means recognizing your flaws and your strengths. Self-awareness is not the same as self-deprecation. Just because you might not like yourself and are good at criticizing does not mean that you are self-aware. If you are truly aware, then you can recognize the good things that you offer to other people and what benefits you provide in this world, too.

Self-awareness also means that you have a high level of self-esteem. It is not to the point that you are arrogant, or narcissistic, but it does give you that boost of energy needed to know that you are a strong, independent person. Self-awareness includes your ability to have confidence and know that you are deserving of the things that come into your life.

The second aspect of emotional intelligence is self-management (AKA self-regulation). This is how you are able to find motivation and trustworthiness within yourself. Can you believe in the things that you say? Are you able to have that level of self-control? Self-management also means that you're able to look at your thoughts and feelings and know how to use them in a positive way. Sometimes, you might have to be adaptable in the situation, you might just have to deal with the change. This is going to be about how you are managing yourself. It's how you can plan and think ahead and determine a positive way to help your future self out. It's how you problem-solve and look at things analytically.

The third aspect is motivation. This is your drive. It's your passion, your ability to recognize your engagement. How involved are you? Are you self-sufficient? Can you find that drive within yourself, and can you bring that out in other people? Motivation isn't just about getting up in the morning and being excited for the day – motivation is looking for meaning. It's recognizing purpose in this life and using that to power you through. It rejuvenates and energizes you.

The fourth aspect is your social awareness (social skills). You might have mastered all these other aspects, but can you say that about other people? Are you able to use your empathy and social skills to recognize how somebody else may be feeling? Can you communicate? Are you good at listening? Are you tolerant of other people? These are all aspects that will be involved in your level of social awareness.

Fifth is your ability to be empathetic. Are you able to collaborate with others? Can you show a high level of conflict management? Are you able to be somebody who can lead and carry those that need it the most? Do you also know how to properly follow other people? When you know how to be an empathetic person and listen to others, you can learn about yourself in the process.

Projection and Deflection

It's important to recognize that we often have many different defense mechanisms to handle any sort of outward aggression that we might be feeling from others. Projection and deflection are two of the most popular defense mechanisms for emotions that you might be having.

Projection is when you take your own feelings and you place them on somebody else. If you are angry at a friend because they haven't been there for you, then you might actually be projecting your own feelings about yourself. Perhaps you are not feeling like you've been very supportive, so you're blaming them because it's too hard for you to admit that it is you who is at fault. You will see this far too often in arguments. Often, what we pick out in other people is what we've already recognized within ourselves. If you project onto somebody else and tell them they are being rude, you might be being rude yourself. Of course, this isn't the case for every time that you're having a discussion with somebody else. However, recognize if you actually believe that they are feeling this or if it is you who is projecting onto others.

Deflection is another common type of defense mechanism. When you deflect, you are avoiding the problem. You are not taking responsibility for that kind of feeling that you are putting on to other people. You might change the argument because it's easier than trying to confront the truth that needs to be faced. If somebody approaches you and tells you that they're upset with you because you were late to their event, you might deflect by saying, "Well, you were late to mine."

That is not a healthy way to manage the disagreement. They might have hurt you, but you can't use that as a weapon against them.

Other types of defense mechanisms include displacement. This is when you might take out your feelings on people that weren't responsible for those emotions. Displacement is easy to do, because we can't often take our frustrations out on the people that deserve them. For example, your boss might be a total jerk, and you hate dealing with them. So you go home and you're rude to your roommate, because it feels good to let out some of that pent-up anger.

You can't do that to your boss or else you might get fired, but your roommate doesn't really have a choice since you both just signed a year-long lease. You then take your anger out on them. This is hard to deal with because we don't always realize we're doing this, and it can really damage relationships.

Denial is also common. This is when you don't believe that something is wrong. You might look for every sort of validation of this not being the truth, whether it's a situation you don't like to be in or something that another person told you. You might deny it because it's just too hard to accept as the truth.

Suppression is when you push your feelings deep down and you don't confront them. You might ignore these emotions by doing something like drinking or doing drugs. You can distract yourself and try to remove your mind from the situation. It's like trying to stuff a dirty closet full of clothes, even though you're past the point where you have any space left. You might just be shoving in there as hard as you can without worrying about what gets broken along the way.

Always look deep into yourself and recognize how your emotions might be used against other people, and how they're hurting you in that process. You are in control of these emotions, so take charge. Don't let them be the things that define you.

Technique #10: Manage Your Anger

Anger can be very challenging to deal with. You'll want to do your best to manage your anger whenever possible.

Still, it's much easier said than done. Remember, anger is a secondary emotion. There is always going to be a deeper underlying reason for why you are feeling this anger. The first thing you can do for anger management is to make sure that you are not blaming anybody else for your anger. The anger is something that could be triggered by an action or an event, but nobody else is standing there, placing this anger in your mind. It is your thoughts which have caused these feelings, not another person. There might be something going on within your head that needs to be confronted. For example, you might be angry at a friend and you lash out on them. If you look deeper, you'll realize that you're not angry – maybe you're just jealous. Maybe you're scared they're leaving you. Maybe you're frustrated that they don't seem like they care enough. Look at the first and the primary emotion behind this anger.

Next, ask about the productivity of this anger. Is it fulfilling something inside of you? Is it helping you achieve a goal? Are you reaching a greater purpose with this anger? Is it fixing the situation? Is it making things better?

Sometimes, anger *can* help us – it might remind us what we're passionate about. It can help drive better emotions.

However, if you don't manage anger, it can control you.

As far as practical tips go, first make sure that you remove yourself from the situation. This is important, especially in the beginning. You might think that you're strong enough to come face-to-face with what makes you angry, but you never know what might trigger you in the moment if you're not careful. Next time somebody makes you angry or frustrated, simply walk away.

Take some time and go in the other room. Approach the topic again after you've cooled down.

Next, make sure that you practice your breathing. Use the breathing exercises that we discussed in the previous step to release the tension in your body. Allow your muscles to become completely relaxed. Feel the tension leave your shoulders to your jaw and anywhere else that you're holding onto stress. From there, it will be up to you to talk it out with whoever you're having the issue with.

Anger is natural, but it is also something that needs to be managed.

Chapter 8

Building a Rock-Solid Routine

Change is all about habit. It took you awhile to get into the habits that you carry around with you now, so it's going to take a little bit to get you out of these, as well. In this chapter, we are going to talk all about the ways that you can effectively add a routine for stress management in your life. This is not something that you can just hope will eventually happen. You can't just expect things to change. You have to be active about it. Create something that you will legitimately stick to. Come up with a realistic plan. Have goals for yourself that provide meaning and value. Make sure that your goals align with your own virtues, and that you're not just basing things off of what other people tell you or expect of you. The more effectively you can create a positive routine, the easier it becomes to actually stick to this in the end.

Laying the Groundwork for an Effective Routine

Once you get into a mindset where you're ready to change and you know how to change, then it's time to establish a routine. You want to create that pattern of repetition, because it's going to be easier to stick to. Also, when you create a routine, it will strengthen your ability to be able to have that high level of emotional strength. The first step for creating a routine is to make sure that you separate your life by importance.

What needs your attention the most? Rank your importance in different ways, as well. Obviously, work is important because it pays your bills, but family is important because it fulfills you. Decide what you are going to commit to these areas of your life each week. You might break it down by having:

- work time
- family time
- creativity moments
- exercise time

- moments where you just do nothing.

You have to remember to schedule in those moments of just sitting around and relaxing, or else you're going to forget to do that. When you do schedule these periods, then anything that you don't get done or miss you could end up doing during that relaxing time. You don't want this to be a constant thing, but if you go a day without having a relaxing moment, that's not the end of the world. Before you implement your routine, you'll want to pay special attention to the one that you already have. This is where a journal can come in handy. Each day, reflect on what you are doing and write down the timestamps of when you do things. It doesn't have to be down to the second, but write down that you had mealtime around 6pm; between 8am and 9pm, you went to work; you went to the gym from 3pm to 4pm; and so on. When you keep track of your day-to-day schedule, then you'll get a good idea of what areas you should be working more on and what areas can be cut down. You might discover that you actually spend two hours in the middle of the day doing nothing at all, even though it felt like you were working because you had your computer open and were attempting to get things done.

Pay attention to what your routine is now so that it gets better in the future. Recognize the flaws and where you need to grow. After you've kept track of what you have been doing, it's time to switch this up and create a new schedule. It's important that you don't completely change to the point where your life is going to be dramatically different. Any sort of extreme change like that can trigger you out of that motivated mindset and you might fall into a place where you are unable to actually commit to this new schedule. If you, right now, just go to work and come home and do not do much, then you can't expect that tomorrow you're going to be able to go to the gym for an hour a day, and then go to a dance class, and then go to an art class, and then have time to hang out with friends, and so on. It's going to be a gradual growth, and you want to incorporate a routine that is somewhat similar to what you do now – just the enhanced version.

After you've created your routine, come up with a challenge for yourself. Pick out something that will make you either think or work a little harder. Maybe you sign up for a new class that you've been wanting to go to. Perhaps you start dating again. Maybe you get a membership to some sort of club that you want to participate in. Do something that scares you and have this be incorporated at one point in your week. As time goes on, you can gradually increase how many scary activities you're doing. The point of this routine is to make sure that you are sticking to a consistent schedule for stress management, so if at any time you're feeling overwhelmed, then you need to learn how to cut back. Setting this routine is going to be very important for your stress management.

Practicing Patience

Patience is going to be your best friend in this journey. It is never easy to start something new, because your brain isn't quite used to it yet. You have to start being more patient so that it becomes easier to implement the things that will actually improve your life. There are a few steps you can take to become a more patient person.

The first thing you can do is make sure that you stop and breathe. If you never give yourself those moments, then it can feel like you're very rushed. When we go from one thing to the next, to the next, to the next, with no break, it makes us feel like we are constantly going.

A car that never turns off is going to die faster than one has moments of rest in between. Make sure that you take five minutes to sit on the couch before running back out after you get home from work. Have moments before you go to sleep where you can calm down instead of expecting to hop right into bed and fall asleep.

Patience is something that needs to be practiced with other people. Take time to stop and truly listen to them. Don't just hear the things that they're saying, but really try to understand the messages they're sharing. Forgive other people and pause before responding to the things that they say. The more you practice patience with other people, the easier it will be to have that willpower with yourself.

Having a routine is essential for your stress management, and you want to do everything in your power to live a happy and healthy life. You can't do this if you're constantly on the go without ever taking a break. Give yourself the chance to decompress and become somebody who can embrace change, because they're not afraid of waiting for good things to come. Life is not a race, it's a journey. You have to enjoy every single step of the way.

You have to begin to improve yourself in order to make sure that you are effectively living the life that you want. This doesn't happen overnight. It's not the click of a button, and it's not a light switch. It's a seed that you're planting now and it's going to take time to grow. Just like a plant, you don't have to just be excited for the end – you can enjoy every single growth stage as it develops.

Technique #11: Focus on Your Sleep

You have to start getting better sleep. Sleep is one of the main reasons you're probably not managing your stress properly. It could be that you're simply tired. Focus on your sleep to give yourself the best chance possible to actually enjoy your day. There are a few tips that you can use in order to improve your sleep.

The first is to come up with an actual schedule. It's great to be able to go to bed when you're tired and wake up when you're rested, but unfortunately, most of our schedules don't allow this kind of flexibility. You have to have a bedtime. It's not just something for children, of course.

Set a bedtime that works best with your schedule. Your brain won't know the difference between 10pm and 10:05pm, but it will know if you're not giving it that proper resting period. Come up with a general time to go to bed based on what time you have to wake up.

Make sure that you give yourself at least seven hours of sleep a night, up to nine. Anything less or more than that might not be as great for your health. Don't give yourself exactly seven hours of sleep, either. If you get into bed at midnight and have to wake up at 7am, then there's going to be a few minutes here and there that can drag the day and make you feel even more tired. Go to bed at 11:45 and wake up at 7:15, to give yourself that little buffer period. You're not going to instantly fall asleep as soon as your head hits the pillow.

After you've come up with your bedtime, make sure that you start your routine based around your shower (if you prefer to shower at night instead of the morning). Make sure that you've stopped drinking any sort of caffeine at least six hours before this time period, as well. It may not seem like it, but having caffeine can make your mind stay active, even if you do manage to fall asleep.

Try to reduce how much you're eating before bed, as well, at least an hour before your bedtime. If you can do two hours, that's even better.

Drink water, and make sure that you take some water to bed with you that you can drink as soon as you wake up in the morning.

You also want to make sure that you cut out screen time at least 30 minutes before bed. If you're on your phone right until the moment that you fall asleep, this is going to keep your mind active. It's going to hurt your eyes and it's going to be harder to get that deep sleep needed for proper rest.

Make sure you have all the lights off. If you are somebody who's a little bit more afraid of the dark and you don't like falling asleep in pitch black, you could get a nightlight, but just make sure that it's a softer color. If you do have to have the TV on as you fall asleep, make sure that you set the timer so it's not on all night. Eventually, you should get to a point where you don't have the TV on at all. But if it is something that comforts you in the beginning, just make sure that you're using a timer so it's not on all night.

As far as waking up goes, make sure you get up as soon as your alarm clock goes off. Too many people will set 10 alarms and then they'll wake up every five minutes within the span of an hour. This is only making things worse. You might think that it helps you and that you feel better, but it really makes everything so much more challenging.

As soon as that first alarm goes off, you should be getting out of bed. Don't hit the snooze button over and over again. The more you do this, the more difficult you're making it for yourself. You're just putting your body in and out of sleep. You need a solid deep sleep, and anything more is just going to make you even more tired.

Give yourself time before having to go to work, as well. It can seem so annoying to have to do this, and you've probably heard it plenty of times before, but you should have around 20 to 30 minutes to relax before going to work.

When you rush right into it, it makes you feel like you are in such a hurry, it only adds to your stress and makes everything worse. If you have to leave your house by 7:45, wake up at 7:10 at the latest. Take your morning shower, if that's what you prefer. Have some coffee, drink some water, brush your teeth, and just sit there and let your mind wake up. If you go, go, go from the moment that you wake up, it makes you feel rushed, overwhelmed, and stressed.

The final tip we're going to talk about is drinking water. Make sure that you drink water every day right when you wake up. This helps kickstart your mind and keeps you hydrated so that you're less lethargic first thing in the morning. You might find that drinking water can be as energizing as drinking a glass of coffee. It might not last you as long as coffeedoes, but it still provides a good relief.

Always look for ways to improve your sleep, because this is going to affect your stress much more than you could even imagine.

Chapter 9

Finding Focus in a Distracting World

There are endless distractions in this world. The upside to this is that, no matter what, you'll always have things to entertain you. The downside is you'll always have things to distract you. To live a focused life is not one that is free from distraction. To live in a world where you can have mental clarity means that you know how to prioritize your thoughts.

Sometimes, this means changing your outside world. Other times, it means simply organizing the things that you think and feel. In this chapter, we're going to cover what it is that you need to have better attention in a world that is so distracting.

Setting Time Aside Every Day for Creative Thinking

You should be setting a time every single day to be creative. Whether it's in the morning or at night, pick a time when you already feel like you are the most creative. Having a moment at night before bed is a good time to start, because this is often when our minds are going wild. You're about to go to sleep, and your brain is getting rid of everything that you don't need from the day.

It's processing all the new information that you've learned and it's cycling through all the thoughts that you've shared. It can be a way to quiet your brain before going to sleep.

You might also want to do it right in the morning. This is also a great time because you have so many dreams from the night before, and you can grab a journal and just start writing about all of the different ones that you've had. You're not limited to just these times, either – do what is best for you!

There are many different ways that you can inspire creativity. Start by having some sort of inspiration or image board. Go through old magazines, take pictures and print them out, and use sketches and find everything in between that inspires you.

Have this board be something that you can revisit. You can put it up on your wall or you can simply keep it in your journal. This can be where you go when you are lacking motivation and looking for more creativity. Take your creativity outside. Of course, if you're doing it at night, it might not be the best time to go outside, but seek moments of creativity out in the wild. Go to the park and people watch. Go for walks and look at nature. Sit in a storefront cafe and notice people passing on the street. Put yourself in these immersive experiences so that you can let your creativity flourish. Make sure your journal is both artistic and something that you can experiment with. You want to give yourself a chance to really get out there and find new information that you can't discover while sitting at home. Enjoy different solitary moments.

You also want to make sure that you have creativity in socialization. If you have other creative friends, it's a great time to share these moments with them. Take art classes together. Have them come over and sit with you while you write. Come up with ideas for shows, movies, and books together. Whatever you do, get social, because not only does that help you stay accountable, but it can actually grow your creativity. If you're all sitting together and sharing different thoughts and ideas, then you might come up with things you wouldn't have, had you been alone.

Listen to the creative processes of the people that you are most inspired by. It's easy to pick out your favorite movie, TV show, book, or song, but you should go beyond just using that for inspiration. Look into how the artist goes through their process. You should also be taking your creative moments and putting them out there for other people to see. Let others give you feedback. They can share things about your art to help you grow. Make sure you challenge yourself to do creative things that make you feel a little uncomfortable. If you're somebody who enjoys drawing but is terrible at painting, then force yourself to paint, maybe once a month. You can learn about yourself through the activities that are making you uncomfortable.

You also want to make sure that you are always practicing. Too many people think that they can't be creative because when they do something, it doesn't turn out as they expected. No good painter only painted their most famous paintings. They probably have so many that we've never seen that they threw away. Some of these might have been good pieces that they just didn't believe in, and others were just practice. The only way for you to get better is for you to try things and learn what you need to improve on and what is fine as it is.

Expose yourself to new activities. Order something different off the menu. Watch a movie you never thought you would see. Go to the library and pick up books that you've never even heard of. Expose yourself constantly, because this is going to keep your brain active.

Play games. Have fun with friends. Play with your pets. Take your kids to the park and play with them, don't just sit on the benches. Just get out in the world and be more creative. It's not always about having productive time. Sometimes, it's just having that time where your creativity can flourish. Creativity is not just painting and sketching, writing, singing, drawing, and so on. Creativity is cooking. It's gardening, it's building, it's designing, it's analyzing, it's reflecting, it's journaling, it's researching. As long as you are doing things for the sake of growth and exploration, that can be creative in itself.

When Multitasking is Bad

With all the suggestions that we gave you for how you can begin to improve your life, you might be feeling a little overwhelmed. It can be easy to want to do everything in the world. We live on this incredible Earth, and there are so many options for what we can start to do. That being said, it's important that you don't multitask, all the time. Some activities, you'll be able to multitask with.

For example, you can listen to podcasts while you're cooking. You can watch a movie while you clean. You can listen to music as you knit. However, you don't want to split too many tasks up, because that can really mess up your perspective. It seems like you might be getting as many things done as possible when you're multitasking, but actually, you can be diverting your attention and making it harder for you to really focus.

Don't give 50% to two different tasks at the same time; give 100% to one task at a time. When you are multitasking, there's a pretty good chance that you're actually not multitasking at all.

It might feel like you're getting more done, but in reality, you might be overlooking some things that needed more attention. Even something as simple as texting while you're walking down the street can really split up your attention. Just take the time to stop, step aside, send the text, and then keep walking.

If you were to take your phone and turn it on and off and on and off throughout the day, you might run out your battery faster than if you just kept it on the whole time. When you're multitasking, you're not always giving attention to two things at once you're going back and forth in between the two. You're turning your focus on and off and on and off for each of those tasks. Simply set time aside to focus only on one thing at once. Multitasking is also bad because it can split your attention and make it harder for you to be interested in things around you.

For example, maybe you always like to have your laptop open while you watch movies. Maybe you're constantly playing games while you have movies playing in the background. You're not going to be fully paying attention to either of these things and instead, it's splitting up your focus. Something like watching games and watching movies isn't necessarily an important task that needs 100% of your attention, but it is an example of how you can diminish your capacity to find interest in some of these things. They have less meaning.

You'll be less engaged, and therefore you won't be able to take away as much from these. Multitasking can actually slow you down if you're not even realizing how it actually splits your focus. What could take you an hour to do for one thing, and an hour to do for another thing, might take you three hours to do both things. Multitasking means that you're not giving your full attention, so you might end up making mistakes at the same time.

That kind of overwhelming feeling of going back and forth, making mistakes, and missing certain aspects can really stress you out. It can make you feel overwhelmed and exhausted if you're not careful. You may also find that you don't remember these tasks as well.

Back to that game and movie example: the next day, you might find you don't even really remember what happened during that movie. When you get used to splitting your focus like this, it means that might be how you treat other people. When somebody is talking to you, you might look down at your phone instead of actually listening to them. All of these could negatively impact your attention, and your ability to take something valuable from these moments. If you're not carefully paying attention, then you can overlook important aspects of mindfulness that might help to actually reduce your stress.

Technique #12: Learn to Say "NO!"

Okay, you don't have to learn how to scream – saying it should do just fine. Still, it's important that we emphasize just how much you might be struggling to really stand up for yourself in a world with constant demands.

The first step in getting better at saying no is making sure that you have a clear vision of why you want to say no. Sometimes, you can lead with the reason, which can make it feel less like you're turning them down. For example, if somebody asks you if you can go out to dinner and you have a different event planned that night, rather than saying, "No, I can't go I have an event," say, "I'm actually going to this event, and I would love to come but I already had this scheduled."

Doing this softens the blow so then you won't feel guilty later on about saying no. Of course, you should never feel guilty, but that is often one of the reasons why we struggle to say no when we want to. Remind yourself that saying no is perfectly fine. Too often, we feel like we have to please all of the other people in our lives, while overlooking our own needs. It's time for you to make sure that you check in with yourself and do everything possible to feel better. Sometimes, we get afraid of saying no because we don't want people to leave us. Maybe you're fearful that once you start saying no, other people won't come into your life as often.

Maybe you don't want to turn them down or disappoint them.

First and foremost, check in with yourself and see if there is some sort of issue from childhood or as you were raised, which makes you feel as though you need to please other people to keep them around. Maybe your parents had really high expectations of you. Perhaps you experienced neglect from a parent, so you went out of your way to try and gain their approval. Whatever it might be, there could be an underlying reason as to why it is so difficult for you to say no to other people. If you're a people-pleaser, it could be from having low self-esteem, or depending on others for your emotional state. The more you choose to please other people, the easier it is to say yes to demands you might not even be able to meet. Don't be afraid that people are going to leave you. They won't. And if they do, good riddance!

You don't need people in your life that are only using you because you are a "yes man." These people are not appreciating you – they're taking advantage of you. Don't let that happen anymore. Sometimes, if you can't say no face to face, then at least say maybe. It's better than saying yes and backtracking later. Let them know that you have to think about it. If somebody doesn't give you that period to think about things, then they're trying to rush you, forcing you to say yes because they know that you're more willing to do so. They might be using speed as a tactic because they understand that if you have time to think about it, you'll definitely say no. Tell them you'll let them know, but you need to check in with a friend or a partner or somebody else first to make sure that you're not saying yes too soon. Other people should understand – and again, if they don't, then good riddance.

We also have to remember to stop offering things. It might feel like you're saying no or yes in a certain situation, but perhaps you are the one to offer the help in the first place. Remind yourself that other people are not going to dislike you just because you're not helping them. The ones that matter the most will be there, regardless of whether you say yes or no.

Technique #13: Minimize Everything

Minimalism started as an art movement as a rejection to the stuffy academic side of art in the 1960s. It was a simplistic form that focused on material and abstract art, in order to convey various messages. Since then, it has grown into a lifestyle. Minimalism is popular now as a reaction to the consumerism that exists within our capitalist society. We are constantly being bombarded with things to buy. Whether it's products at the store that are buy-one-get-one-free or sales that offer up discounts when you purchase in bulk, we are in a consumerist society that promotes buying as much as possible. The focus is on getting as much for your money as you can in the form of quantity, while completely ignoring quality.

One thing you can do to reduce distraction and help improve your focus is to try and emulate some aspects of minimalism. You can start by decluttering your home. Look at the things you've been keeping around. Often, what is physically in our house is a mental manifestation of some deep underlying thoughts. For example, if you look at the state of your bedroom, that alone can reveal the state of your mind. Is it clean, structured, and organized? Is it messy, with a bunch of ideas left behind? Is it dirty and neglected? Look at your space and try and reflect and evaluate what it might be trying to tell you about yourself.

After this, start to look at clutter and see what this could represent. You might have boxes and boxes and boxes of memories. It's always good to hold on to some parts of our past, because it can bring up good emotions. However, you should limit it to just a few boxes, because anything more than that is likely unnecessary. Perhaps you're keeping around whole objects and large pieces of furniture simply because it provides you a memory.

You don't have to go out and throw everything away, but don't keep things around just because of the thoughts they bring up. Maybe you have a closet full of old dirty t-shirts that you don't even wear anymore, but you're too afraid to let them go. You might not even have to throw them away, but maybe you could find a better use for them. Perhaps you could cut them up and take the logos to make a nice quilt, and use the rest as rags for cleaning. Look for alternate ways to use things if you're too afraid to throw them away at first. For larger memories, you can also simply take pictures. Since we can digitize pictures, you can keep folders and folders on your computer of all these memories. While that might still be cluttering, it is better on your computer than in your closet taking up so much physical space. When you have so much clutter, it does take up some of your brain power. That pile of unread books in the corner is a constant reminder of unfinished projects. Even though you don't actively think about those books as your eyes scan the room, you still pick up on them, and part of your brain will go towards processing that information. Don't leave old projects around, because it's just a reminder of guilt. You should do your best to try and finish those projects as you start to minimize. Then, you can give yourself a time limit. Tell yourself, "I have to finish this within a week, or else I'm going to throw it away." If you can't make time for it at that point, it's probably fine to just toss it because anything important, you'd make time for.

You can also sell or give away half-finished projects, too, because somebody else might be able to pick up where you left off. Just because it's not done doesn't mean that it's trash, but that also doesn't mean that you should be keeping it around.

The most important areas for you to declutter are your closet, your bathroom cabinets, your kitchen cabinets, your attic or basement, and anywhere else that has an easily accessible place to collect a bunch of junk. The more you can minimize your space, the easier it will be to minimize your mind.

Reflect on the thoughts you're having and see if they are important to keep around or if there are things that you can simply let go of. Frequently, we will carry memories with us that we no longer need. These include negative thoughts and guilty rumination. Free your mind by doing things like practicing mindfulness and incorporate more meditation. When you meditate, you'll be able to take moments to really cleanse your mind.

Start by sitting somewhere comfortable and focus on your breathing. As thoughts come into your brain, push them out until you're not thinking of anything at all. Picture your thoughts as if they were leaves floating by on a stream. You can pick those leaves up, or you can just let them simply flow on past. You don't need to push them out of the way, just watch them as they drift from one end to the other.

Try to meditate for at least two minutes. When you first start, it can seem easy to just sit there and think about nothing for two minutes, but it can actually be a challenge to really let your mind go blank. After you've managed to do this, gradually increase the time until you can make it to 30 minutes or even an hour.

If you're having trouble doing this at first, there are plenty of guided meditation audiobooks or videos online that will take you through the process. The more you meditate, the easier it will be to mentally declutter.

Chapter 10

Maintaining the Important Balance Between Work and Life

If only we had unlimited time, we'd have so much less to worry about. Unfortunately, time does run out, so we want to know how to make the most of it. If we could, we'd spend all day long hanging out with friends and enjoying different activities. Unfortunately, we do have to work, so it's all about maintaining balance.

Cutting Yourself Off From Technology

Social media is something that can really dig its claws into us and cause so much unnecessary anxiety. If you are struggling with social media, then it's time to take a break. You don't have to delete everything right now. However, you do need to start giving yourself social media blackout days. Of course, you probably already go through your day without checking your social media for several hours. However, you need to take moments of reflection to specifically block out social media. Create rules for yourself.

Tell yourself no social media as you're sitting there eating dinner. Maybe it's when you're having family movie night. Put your phone away and really focus on the present moment. How many times have you opened Instagram, closed it, and then opened it again without even thinking about it? We use social media mindlessly. That is something that we should be including more thoughtfully.

Social media doesn't have to be demonized, either. It's not about rejecting it entirely. It can help you stay connected to other people. At the same time, it's also something that can cause so much stress and anxiety. Make sure that you are only following people on social media that provide you happiness or joy.

Make a rule right now to unfollow at least 10 people that don't provide you happiness. Even if they are friends or family members, if you don't enjoy the things that they're posting, then you have no obligation to follow them. If somebody notices you unfollowed them and they confront you about it, then just be honest with them that you're focusing your attention on something else at the moment.

You might have been used to following people who post a different selfie every single day. Maybe you don't really enjoy seeing that, because it's the same picture over and over again and they highly edit their photos to the point that it makes you feel bad about yourself. Simply unfollow them – block them, even, if you have to – and instead follow things that boost your self-esteem and help promote creativity.

Pick out 10 new Instagram accounts to follow that you enjoy. If you don't have an Instagram, then pick out something on a different social media. Follow a cool page that has a bunch of facts about science. Follow an artistic page. Follow a chef who posts their videos. Follow somebody who shares positive quotes or affirmations.

Whatever it is, pick out something that actually makes you feel good, rather than keeping up with people who only cause you more anxiety. We have to remember that the people online are altering their pictures and creating a perspective. They're not showing you the entire story. Even if they have videos, they're editing them in order to follow a specific progression. If you don't realize the reality that lies behind some of the pictures that are being taken, it can really eat away at your self esteem. Cut yourself off and make time just to focus on yourself. After this, make sure that you begin to cut yourself off from checking emails or texts. Of course, if you want to check texts from friends, that's fine. But remember that many options on your phone will enable you to snooze notifications from certain people specifically. If your boss is texting you later in the day, you do not have to respond. They shouldn't be texting you outside of your work hours, anyway. If somebody is emailing you, then turn off notifications for this. One of the best things you can do for yourself is to turn off notifications from things like Slack, Gmail, LinkedIn, and any other form of messaging that might be sending you different notes throughout the day.

Of course, if it's really going to affect your work performance, then keep up with the emails and text, but still make sure that you schedule a time to completely turn off your notifications. You can also turn your phone into airplane mode to stop you from getting phone calls. It is okay to not answer. If you're constantly checking these things, it can make you feel like you are always at work. You are not your job, even if you went to school for and dedicated over a decade of education trying to get to the position that you have – you still do not have to be on the job at all times. You're still a person, at the end of the day. You're still somebody that just wants to eat or watch TV or sleep in peace. Allow yourself to do this and remind yourself you're deserving of those moments. It's okay to turn your phone off, and you might have to schedule these blackout periods to ensure that you're actually following through with this process.

Maintaining Balance

It's important that we talk about maintaining balance. This means balancing work life, social life, family time, and personal time. Too often, we overlook that we need to schedule time alone. It can be scary sometimes, but you do have to do it. It is only in these moments of reflection that you will really be able to look deep at yourself and improve on the things that you need to work on. When you are alone, you can fully appreciate the people that you are not around at the moment. If you constantly surround yourself with other people, you might not fully appreciate them, because you're so overwhelmed by their consistent presence.

First, make sure that you focus on work time. Often, this is something that you don't always have control over the schedule of. If you work hourly, then that is your exact schedule. Don't go beyond that. If you're somebody that freelances and creates your own schedule, make sure that you come up with one that works for you. A lot of people will go for the nine-to-five life, but if that's not something that interests you, it's totally fine to create your own schedule.

Do whatever works best for you in the moment. After this, make sure that you are scheduling social time. When are you going to be meeting up with friends? Even on weeks that you might not want to go out at all, you should force yourself at least once to get out there and spend time with at least one friend. This way, you always maintain a certain level of social activity. After this, schedule in family time. This includes the people that are in your immediate family. It might be your husband, your wife, your daughter, or your son. Make sure that you plan daily activities with them, even if the activity is just sitting on the couch together watching TV. After this, schedule in your personal time. Do not overlook this aspect, even though it seems like one that you don't need to focus on. We all need to have moments where we can just relax and be ourselves. You want to be able to let loose without the pressure of talking to anybody.

You need to be alone with your thoughts so that you can work through them in a healthy way. Go on dates with yourself. It's okay to take your kids to a babysitter just to get out and go shopping alone. Take turns with your spouse. Watch the kids while one of you goes and does the grocery shopping alone. Go to a movie or sit down at a restaurant by yourself. We need these moments because we have to improve our relationship with ourselves. If you're not nurturing that, then it can have negative impacts, just like not nurturing a friendship might. You should be somebody that you enjoy being around, and this can only be done when we take that time to really get to know ourselves.

Being Kind

Being kind is a great way to make everything, from work life to family life, more balanced. When you have kindness, gratitude, and positivity through everything you do, it really helps to manage your stress. Always look for ways that you can be kinder to yourself and to other people. Share things. Do little tasks without people knowing. Buy gifts for people, even when it's not a holiday.

Leave your extra quarters at the laundromat. Pay for the food of the person behind you at the drive-thru. Look for these little moments of kindness and it can make you feel more fulfilled.

You should also be practicing gratitude. Gratitude means that you are thankful and appreciative for everything in your life. It's not as though you are overly excited about everything, but an acknowledgement that even the bad stuff has helped to shape you who you are.

When you show gratitude in your life, it helps to shift your perspective from looking at what you don't have and instead focusing on all that you do. It's easy to think about all the stuff that we want to buy while ignoring everything that already surrounds us. You might want a bigger house, but we should be grateful that we even have a house in the first place. You might want a better job, but we have to be grateful that we have the job that we do. Don't make yourself feel guilty for not being appreciative. But just remember that this mindset will help elicit greater feelings in you later on.

The more you develop this kindness and gratitude, the easier it will be to find peace within yourself. That is the power that is really going to help you find balance, serenity, and calmness in your brain.

Technique #14: Work on Communication and Listening

One important thing that can help you effectively manage and reduce your stress is to make sure that you have proper communication. This doesn't mean just knowing how to share your feelings with other people. You also have to look for ways to make yourself a better listener. Too frequently, we are focused on what we are going to say rather than actually listening to the other person. When you listen to other people, don't just act like you're listening. Don't sit there and think about what you want to show them. As you listen and start to fully invest in everything that they are sharing with you, refrain from reacting right away. Take a moment to really process the words that are coming out of their mouth. Try to listen to their story and what it is that they're sharing.

If you find that you're struggling to pay attention and really listen to somebody, then take a moment to practice mindfulness. Look at their eyes. Look at their cheeks. Look at their chin. Do a scan from the top of their head to the bottom of their face to pick up on what cues they might be giving you with the way that they look.

When you do this, you're effectively making it easier to focus on the things they have to share. Don't come up with what you're going to plan next. Too often, we're listening and picking up only on the things that are going to help us prove a point.

Conversations are not competitions, they're chances to get to know and better understand each other. If you're too focused on just trying to make your point and have your agenda shared, then you're not fully grasping the things they are trying to express.

Ask questions as often as you can. When you ask questions, not only does it make it easier for you to understand what they're saying, but it shows them that you're legitimately listening to what they're sharing. The better you communicate with other people, the easier it will be for them to share things with you.

Technique #15: Laugh and Smile

At the end of the day, laughing and smiling is a great way to reduce stress. Laughing is good for you and it's good for the people around you. Smiling can actually decrease the production of cortisol in your body and lower your blood pressure. It also can boost the production of serotonin and dopamine, which are feel-good hormones. Smiling also makes you look appear younger and more attractive to other people.

Take Control Of Your Day

Now, next time you are feeling blue, go stand in front of the mirror and just smile. If this doesn't help make you feel any better, then force yourself to laugh. This can trick your brain into thinking that you're happy. You deserve to have fun and enjoy your life.

Smile when you talk. Smile when you share. Smile when you listen. The key is making sure to smile with your entire face. Don't just move your cheeks; your eyes should be squinted, too. As you smile, show your teeth and open your mouth slightly. You'll be amazed at how a good smile can really be a powerful tool for navigating through this world.

Smiling and laughing also helps to reduce your stress and make you feel better. If you can't force yourself to laugh or smile, go on YouTube and look up whatever funny video you laugh at the most. Even if it's just 30 seconds, that can be enough to boost hormones that will make you feel good throughout your day.

Conclusion

Stress is natural. We will never be able to completely rid our lives of stress, no matter how much emphasis is put on the management of our emotions. We will always have some stressful responses where we just act on the emotions that pull at our heartstrings the most. Maybe you realize you forgot something at home. Perhaps you have a quarrel with a coworker. Maybe you have experienced the loss of a loved one. These things are inevitable, and we will have stressful responses. Anyone who doesn't ever experience stress in their lives is simply not paying enough attention to their emotions!

While this might sound scary to some, it doesn't have to be. Stress is inevitable, but it is also something that we can manage. It's just like anything else that needs balance in life. You will always need money, but if you're smart and know how to manage it well, that shouldn't be a problem. You will always need to eat food, but if you're smart and have knowledge and control over nutrition, you don't have to worry about this being unhealthy. Bad things will happen, but if we know how to properly manage our emotions, it won't be so scary.

It's all about identification. You have to know where these thoughts are coming from, if you ever want to have proper control over them. Did someone else light the fuse of stress within you? Were your thoughts something that developed over time? Is this a momentary instance, or a habitual thought process that needs fixing? When you can identify these, it becomes easier to manage the feelings and emotions that used to have complete control over you.

Nobody is perfect – we've heard that one plenty of times. No one ever will be perfect, either. Still, it is a concept we are obsessed with. Perfection can be the state in which you do things, not necessarily an end goal. So long as you are putting 100% of your effort towards everything that you do with a willingness to accept your flaws and work on your mistakes, then you could be considered perfect. We all just have to do the best that we can with the things that we have.

The sooner you realize that there will always be things which are out of your control, the quicker you will be able to make peace with yourself. It can exhaust us quickly when we try to change the unchangeable. It's like hitting a brick wall with a rubber hammer. It's pointless, and will only tire us through the process. Focus instead on looking at the way that you can work around this brick wall with the tools you have, rather than trying to make these tools you work on something that won't be affected.

Mental health and physical health aren't always linked together, but they very much go hand in hand. Your hormones are responsible for everything in this life, and they play a huge role in the way that you are able to manage your thoughts and feelings. If we overlook just how much our hormones will affect us, it can have grave consequences. The things you eat and the way you move your body will help to regulate every other aspect of your health.

The way we talk to ourselves can be very damaging. You are going to be your own biggest critic. That's not always a bad thing, as personal reflection and growth is essential for happier health. However, if we don't limit the things we say, we can turn into a bully rather quickly. Always look deep within yourself and challenge the thoughts that you do have. You might feel powerless when you are constantly critical of yourself, but in reality, this is one of the few things you have complete power over.

Your mindset is yours to control, not one that is going to be shaped by other people. As an autonomous individual, you have the power to decide which thoughts you'll let flourish and which ones you might choose to ignore. Though it might seem that others are affecting the way we feel, it will always be you who gets to decide your emotional state at the end of the day.

From the moment that we were born, emotion dictated our lives. It's not easy for adults to manage the thoughts and feelings they have, so we can be certain that children will struggle with this in the same way. Even though you might never have been given the tools needed to power through your emotions as a child, you are in charge of the way you share things now. You get to pick and choose how you are going to react to various situations.

It's all about routine. It took a while to develop the brain that you have now, so it's going to take just as long to change that for good. It's important that you have patience and practice living in peace with yourself as you navigate through your growth mindset. This is a very routine world, so we have to remember that it's all about habits. Even the smallest change can be the first stepping stone towards a greater and more prosperous life.

With so many distractions in the world, it can be easy to fall off these habits you've created and get trapped in a mindset that works against you. Maintaining focus and direction is exactly what is needed to ensure you are going in the right direction. Set time aside to do the things you enjoy. Schedule moments where you don't have to do anything at all. Find ways to cut down unnecessary fluff in your life that doesn't actually provide you any sort of fulfillment.

Life is about balance, and you are the only one who can determine its stability.

You will get there. You will still have days where everything feels terrible, and your life won't be free from moments of fear and anxiety. With the right tools and a focused mind, though, you can choose whether you'll let these aspects destroy you or create the strong person that you are.

References

Banschick, M. (2015). Regret – 8 Ways to Move On. Retrieved from https://www.psychologytoday.com/us/blog/the-intelligent-divorce/201505/regret-8-ways-move

Berg, A. (n.d.). The State of Fashion 2017. Retrieved from https://www.mckinsey.com/industries/retail/our-insights/the-state-of-fashion

Business Wire. (2019). The $72 Billion Weight Loss & Diet Control Market in the United States, 2019-2023 - Why Meal Replacements are Still Booming, but Not OTC Diet Pills - ResearchAndMarkets.com Retrieved from https://www.businesswire.com/news/home/20190225005455/en/72-Billion-Weight-Loss-Diet-Control-Market

Cherry, K. (2019). 20 Common Defense Mechanisms Used for Anxiety. Retrieved from https://www.verywellmind.com/defense-mechanisms-2795960

Grohol, J. (2019). 15 Common Defense Mechanisms. Retrieved from https://psychcentral.com/lib/15-common-defense-mechanisms/

Hall, M. (2013). I do… cost a lot: Weddings by the numbers. Retrieved from https://www.cnn.com/2013/08/09/living/matrimony-by-the-numbers/

Psychology Today. (n.d.). Self-Esteem. Retrieved from https://www.psychologytoday.com/us/basics/self-esteem

Mayo Clinic. (n.d.). Exercise: 7 benefits of regular physical activity. Retrieved from https://www.mayoclinic.org/healthy-lifestyle/fitness/in-depth/exercise/art-20048389

Selhub, E. (2018). Nutritional Psychiatry: Your Brain on Food. Retrieved from https://www.health.harvard.edu/blog/nutritional-psychiatry-your-brain-on-food-201511168626

Wolff, R. (2018). How US Politics Sustains US Capitalism. Retreived from https://www.commondreams.org/views/2018/08/19/how-us-politics-sustains-us-capitalism

SHUT UP AND FOCUS

19 Highly Effective Time Management Habits for Entrepreneurs

Introduction

A year has 365 days. Everyone knows that. There are 12 months, 52 weeks and 24 hours each day. But let's narrow it down further to just one day at a time. You have exactly 1440 minutes per day. Are you making the most of it?

Hey, Bruce, got a minute?

Yeah, sure... What is it?

Well, there you go. You just wasted a minute in random chit-chat about who Kevin from HR is currently dating.

Tell us this: Did that piece of information add any value to your work? Did it affect your life in some manner? Did it excite or sadden you for some reason? Probably not, unless the one who Kevin was leaving with happens to be your partner.

Jokes apart, the one minute you wasted is something you will never get back. Do you know how much happens in a minute? According to a report by MSN, McDonald's sells over 4,500 burgers a minute, 9,700+ Ubers are booked and 590+ iPhones are sold in a minute worldwide. It puts your gibberish chit-chat to shame, no?

For any entrepreneur, time is of the essence. So you just had an idea, you worked upon it, and now you are finally earning a handsome income. Is that all you aspire to be? Is that all you ever wanted to be? If yes, then you have to drop this book right now and be on your way.

If not, then this will help you do something more. Something that will help you rise in both rank and the eyes of your loved ones. And believe me, there is no secret to it. It is all about managing your time and priorities. One thing even Elon Musk struggles with.

A lot of time is wasted every day doing unproductive work. Work that doesn't bring in any sales, work that doesn't contribute to your health or leaves you with having to compromise on other important areas of your life—your family. If you are one of those entrepreneur dads or partners who is always late to a party or, worse, don't make it just because you are juggling with so much on your plate and don't have time for you or the kids, then this book is for you.

It is also for you if you or your business has been suffering and you keep wondering what you could have done better to improve your sales or generate more profits. It is common knowledge that most of the things we do at the last minute aren't as well thought-out and research-oriented. Think about the last time you went last-minute shopping for Christmas for someone you love. Was your instinct to get them something thoughtful or just get them 'anything' so that you don't have to show up empty-handed? The last-minute tasks are never the best and hold little value. The same applies to business. Anything hasty and conceived at the last minute doesn't hold the appeal something planned does. What delays things is the lack of time. The more time we have to plan things, the more thorough and involved we are. The best outputs and outcomes result where there hasn't been an opportunity cost to pay.

So if it all comes down to time, don't you think you need to learn to manage it?

A normal person's day is broken down into time segments. You need to get to work by a certain time, get to the bank within a specified set of operating hours, go to the grocery, fetch your kids from school and watch them.

Depending on the type of business you own, you may need to speak with clients, set up meetings, finish products, ship them out, etc. Entrepreneurs fulfill a lot of roles in their businesses, and it is very easy to let one task overwhelm the others. This can translate to lost income—because the entrepreneur may end up missing something vital.

You may feel like you never seem to get enough done in a day, that you are always running after something. If you are already knee-deep in your business, you may feel like the clock is running after you.

You need to manage your time to get maximum returns from your mini-investments during the day. These are the minor things that you do during the day that end up adding up and give you a sense of accomplishment.

Knowing what tasks you will be doing for the day, controlling your time can reduce the amount of stress that you experience on a day-to-day basis. Even simple techniques can bring you to a point where the stress is easily managed.

So what is time management, exactly? And why do you need it in your life? Here's what I know and believe in. Managing your time is all about taking control of your life. It is about doing things with the most added value benefits at the end of the day. It is allowing yourself to follow a roadmap, ensuring that every roadblock is handled at a certain time and with efficiency.

The first thing you must remember is that time management is a skill. Great!

Unlike talents, everyone can learn a new skill. Skills are trainable. Have you ever tried your hand at something new? Perhaps, you learned a new language? Was it not difficult at first? Didn't you want to give up? But eventually, when you stuck with it, you learned it. Today, speaking that language might feel like a habit. Any new habit becomes as easy as breathing once it is practiced enough. So is the case with time management. But for every new habit, you need to get rid of the destructive ones first. Sadly, we live in an age where information and technology are linked undeniably, which leaves us with waves of knowledge that is of no use to us.

Imagine you decided to wake up early so that you can catch up on some fresh air and have more time to handle work commitments. To do that, you will need to sleep early. If you are someone who has the habit of watching TV before bed or wasting time browsing social media, you will have to give it up or else your sleep and health will be compromised. Thus, to adopt good habits, you need to forgo a bad one.

And after some time it will feel more like a lifestyle than practice, and that is the goal of this whole book.

Most entrepreneurs, like myself, have complained about a lack of time and organization. Sometimes it is their family that has to suffer and other times, the business. Since either can't be taken for granted or expected to sprout without you, your job is to find the middle ground: a way that prioritizes things in an order where nothing gets neglected. I want you to have no guilt at the end of the day. There shouldn't be an opportunity cost that you should pay just because of your lack of organization and management. Your kids shouldn't have to miss a parent on their birthday because they are stuck with some pending work that should have been completed days before.

In this book, together we shall learn about 19 such highly effective habits that are going to help you generate more revenue for your business and also give your family and friends the time they deserve. Meaning, neither of the two will have to suffer. I have personally adopted these, and I have seen the magnitude of what grander change it can bring into your life. Why do I call them highly effective, you might wonder? It is because these have proven to hold worth and allow you, as a struggling

entrepreneur, to manage both your workload as well as other important affairs without looking at your watch from time to time, thinking where the hell did I waste so many hours of the day?

Each habit is simple, doesn't need a lot of effort on your part, and will be easy to adopt and live by. With these newfound habits, not only will you be able to manage your time properly, but also use that extra time to work on more income-driving habits. So this will not only free up time but make you more money in the long-term.

Let's begin!

Chapter 1: Avoid Procrastination and Finish the Most Urgent Task First

In the first chapter, we shall talk about some of the most pressing and common habits that people have. The first being procrastination and the second, wasting time doing unimportant tasks and failing to accomplish the most important ones.

The first habit that holds you back from your dreamed success as an entrepreneur is your persistence in delaying things until the last minute. You easily fall victim to the word tomorrow. Not only does that sound enticing to you, but it also serves as the wrong kind of motivation. After all, why would you want to delay doing something you can easily do today or right now?

There is some science behind it. Let's learn something about that first!

Habit #1: Avoid Procrastinating

Entrepreneurs are brilliant thinkers with an abundance of ideas, tasks, and projects. If these ideas and projects aren't in the process of implementation already, you can't expect

151

to succeed. So let's begin by calling it an entrepreneur's biggest enemy.

The combination of the two can be deadly, and thus not advisable. In the simplest of terms, you may define procrastination as the act of delaying or avoiding doing things that need to be accomplished. Broadly speaking, it is the practice of choosing more pleasurable things over less pleasurable ones, or accomplishing the less urgent tasks in place of urgent ones—the outcome of which isn't favorable or profitable in the long run.

You might not even realize that while you are getting up for your fourth cup of coffee for the day or wasting time scrolling down your Facebook newsfeed, you are putting your business in second place and your comfort at first. No entrepreneur who does that ever achieves what they dream of.

Your goals and aspirations should always be a priority.

You might think that the age of the internet is to blame for the rise in population of procrastinators, but you are gravely mistaken. Centuries ago, 800 B.C. to be precise, Hesiod, a famous Greek poet of his time, cautioned readers to not put off important things for tomorrow. Even then, he was genius enough to notice the lazy attitude of the people. But, hey, that is just recorded history. What if procrastination existed way before that too? For all we know, the dinosaurs saw the meteorite coming toward them but went back to eating and BAM!

The reason I want to stress this is that not only is procrastination detestable, it is also downright harmful. Studies have proven that procrastination leads to increased levels of stress and reduced well-being (Eerde, 2016). True procrastination is the prime failure of self-regulation. Things don't just randomly get delayed. You have a voluntary role to play in the postponement. Although a poor time concept exacerbates the problem, the poor management of emotions or, to put it better, lack of control over your emotions seems to be the core problem.

There are two schools of thought regarding procrastination. One school regards it as harmful and hateful, while the other looks at it as a positive motivator. The sympathizers believe that the delay in accomplishing tasks can serve as beneficial in helping the doer sort out between the most and less urgent ones. And as long as the important ones get done, it doesn't matter how much time they took. They go as far as calling it working your best under pressure. John Perry, a Stanford philosopher, in his book called The Art of Procrastination finds it crucial to your success. However, he stresses that one must reassess their list of to-dos when short on time and give their fullest to the most important tasks at hand first.

Psychological scientists, on the other hand, find it problematical. They believe that the act of delaying things until the very last minute conflates proactive behaviors as well as the art of prioritizing and replaces it with detrimental and self-defeating habits.

Keeping all that in mind, have you ever thought why do you procrastinate?

Is there some trigger(s)? If so, what could they be?

Adesh Silva

Why are we obsessed with the word "Tomorrow"?

Here are some of the reasons I believe contribute toward the profound admiration for delaying work.

No concrete goals

Having a vague or abstract goal just makes the whole idea of working less interesting (McCrea, Liberman, Trope, & Sherman, 2008). The lack of knowledge or perhaps a vision can make you want to put it off. For instance, you may have decided to start meditation but that is just a vague goal unless you know what you wish to achieve with it. Is it more clarity of your thoughts that you seek or just a clutter-free paradigm to seek new information. Unless you are clear on your goals, you are less likely to take it up. The same applies to tasks.

Hoping For a better option

Another reason why entrepreneurs delay their tasks in the present is that they see a more hopeful and viable option to perform it shortly. It may work in cases where the present lacks the resources and set of skills required, but it fails at some point. It leads to long-term procrastination, which is even worse. Most of the time, the individual just delays the task and ends up with no intended course of action.

Indecisiveness

Sometimes, entrepreneurs procrastinate because they think they are bad at making decisions on time (Tibbetta & Ferrarib, 2015). The delay occurs because the individual wastes too much time in identifying which course of action will be the most profitable and beneficial. The lack of decisiveness just puts things on hold until the very last minute. For instance, you might have a ton of ideas for your next sales campaign, but you might not be able to pick one. The abundance of choices and your inability to categorize them in the order of most beneficial to least beneficial will make the task stressful and tedious.

Distractions

Distraction and procrastination are friends for life. They go hand in hand, scouting on vulnerable entrepreneurs who give in quickly. The moment they spot their prey, they make sure the job is well done. Distraction makes other tasks more interesting than the one at hand. It could be a beeping message, a delightful snacking session or just watching out of your window looking at strangers.

The more distracted you are, the less likely you are to complete an unfinished task and add to your tomorrow's to-do list.

Doubts about control

Sometimes, entrepreneurs procrastinate because they are doubtful about the outcomes of their choices as they hold no control over the input. For instance, you might not want to start on a project that you already know won't get approved or appreciated. No matter how much you try, you just know that you won't be able to accomplish it and that low self-regard leads to procrastination.

Aversion toward tasks

Often the tasks that we don't feel excited about are delayed for a later date in the future. Task aversion is a common yet ignored phenomenon. The majority of us complete tasks because we have to and not because we like to. That very difference is what makes us delay it till the very last minute. Picture this, you need to make an important phone call to someone you know you can't stand. Would you delay it or get it over with. Your first natural response would be to delay it because it doesn't excite you. The more unappealing the task, the lesser chances of it reaching completion.

Perfectionism

When people aim for perfection, they become extremely cautious and self-critical (Pychyl & Flett, 2012). This also becomes one of the reasons for procrastination. You might be so afraid of making a mistake that you might put off trying it all together. The idea of flawing build too much pressure that you become anxious whenever there is a mention of it.

Sensation Pursuing

Lastly, some people also procrastinate because they want to make the task more challenging, add some excitement to it and see how well they do it under pressure (Piers, 2007).

You may have to deliver a presentation to potential clients the following day and you don't start working on it until the night because you want to see if you are strong enough to take up the challenge and risk your chances of success with the newfound thrill plus anxiousness. You may have delayed it because it seemed uninteresting before that and you didn't feel like wasting your time over it.

In some rare cases, it may work out well for you once but it won't all the time. Add to that the additional stress you will experience that may very well hinder your performance while delivering the presentation even though you had it all sorted in your head and on the screen.

Lack of motivation

Another significant reason we procrastinate is that we aren't driven enough to work on a task. We lack the required motivation. When we were growing up, most of the things we did were because we were pressured into doing them. We cleaned our plates, we made our bed, and we went to sleep before midnight. Why? Because we were extrinsically motivated by our parents. Extrinsic motivation is similar to a lack of motivation because there is no intrinsic will to accomplish a task. When we suffer from a lack of motivation or motivated extrinsically, we are likelier to procrastinate (Katz, Eilot, & Nevo, 2014).

Requiring instant gratification

Many of us like to live in the present. Although a monk will tell you of the countless benefits of living in the present, it doesn't work very well when it breeds unhealthy and harmful habits such as procrastination. We all crave instant gratification. We want the results of our marketing campaigns right away. We want to know how well we do in the last quarter even when the next one has just begun. We want to know exactly how much we will be made before the end of this year.

The point being, we are more excited about trying things with an instant reward attached to it. Sometimes it is monetary and most of the time—intangible. Watching meaningless TV will always feel better than working on an Excel Spreadsheet. We prioritize things linked with some short-term gratification and thus procrastinate over things with long-term value. Why? It is because watching TV is more pleasurable in the present.

From procrastinator to productive, knocking out the enemy

Now that we have all the reasons jotted down in our minds, we need to move onto the solution. How can one overcome procrastination and whether if it is an achievable task or not?

Habits are changeable suggests psychology. It may take you some time to overcome something detrimental, but you will eventually overcome it. Sooner than you know, it will feel like a part of you and become natural. I have broken down the process in a few steps, each with a promising potential to get you off your seat and attend to all the pending tasks at once.

Have clearly-defined deadlines

Deadlines are what push us forward. The sooner the deadline, the harder we work. When I started writing this book, I was juggling between two different businesses and my family. Of course, there were setbacks, lack of ideas and low levels of motivation, but the day I assigned myself a deadline to finish it, it changed the whole scenario. I felt more driven, deliberately avoided distractions and set a time to work on the book every day for two hours. Previously, I had no track of where I spent had the 24-hours and doing what, but with a deadline in place, everything changed. I was more cautious about the time spent on each task during the day so that I could go home and work on the book. The result of it is in your hands right now.

Deadlines, whether set by a client or yourself, can significantly boost your productivity an interest in the task.

Coming to the second more crucial aspect of the heading is setting a deadline that isn't too far-fetched. You must have one that is near so that you avoid any chance of falling under the spell of procrastination. The sooner a deadline, the bigger the urgency to complete it.

Break down your goals

You can't achieve everything overnight, so try not to. Each task, whether big or small, requires focus and determination. Having too much on your plate will only lead to confusion, increased stress and fear of failure—the perfect recipe to procrastinate. However, when you break down your goals into achievable milestones, that's a whole different story. You set a fixed time to start on one task and take it to completion with all your might and focus. These little bouts of accomplishments will further oomph your motivation, and once that adrenaline kicks in it's like kryptonite for procrastination.

Stay sane and don't multitask

Multitasking keeps the mind distracted. It may work for some but if you come to think about it, divided attention didn't get anyone any good. You work your best when you are focused on a particular task and putting all your mental and physical efforts toward its completion. When you have too much occupying your mind, there is a possibility that you might want to just give up everything and put it all on hold because it feels too chaotic in your head.

Thus, if the goal is to avoid delaying things, stay focused on just one at a time and give your 100% to it.

Set rewards for your accomplishments

Positive Reinforcement isn't just for pets. Have you ever wondered how did we come up with the concept in the first place? Positive reinforcement works for everyone: kids, teenagers, adults, and seniors. Rewards boost performance as one can convince their mind that something good is going to happen. The same works for procrastination.

Setting rewards for the competition of several tasks is more likely to make you want to complete them. It could be as little as going home an hour early or as big as taking the entire weekend off to visit the beach. The key is to keep you focused on the task and prevent procrastination.

Keep work hours short

Long work hours not only saturates the mind, but it also diminishes our excitement and motivation toward completing a task. This leads to procrastination. Thus, taking short breaks between the tasks is ideal as it keeps your mind refreshed. When the mind is revitalized, even the most mundane of tasks seem doable. For an aspiring entrepreneur, this is highly crucial as motivation is imperative when starting to turn dreams into a reality.

Moreover, during your break time, try not to think about the task. Utilize that time to perform some mental exercises or chit-chat. Constantly, thinking about the task will only make it seem harder and less enjoyable—this makes you procrastinate.

Habit # 2: Finish the Most Important Task First

If you have an important task scheduled for the next day, aim to do it first thing in the morning. Several studies propose that accomplishing the most important tasks first leaves one with a sense of accomplishment, satisfaction, and even joy. It enhances productivity and also boosts confidence. Ernest Hemingway worked on his writing first thing upon waking up. According to him, it happens to be the most peaceful time of the day and there is no disturbance to abrupt the flow of writing. His story and many other similar stories of famous authors, entrepreneurs, athletes, and actors are quoted in Daily Rituals: How Artists Work by Mason Currey (Currey, 2013). It is a great read if you are fascinated with how your inspirational idols do things.

If there is a correlation with productivity and accomplishment of important tasks, shouldn't you, as an entrepreneur, who has a million things to accomplish in the limited number of hours, learn it and swear by it for eternity?

Yes, I thought so too!

Well, I am going to be straightforward with you here. The tip is nothing but trying to accomplish the most important or urgent task first thing in the morning. Like any other entrepreneur, you must have a to-do list for the day. On that list, there must be some tasks requiring urgency, some tasks that aren't that urgent and some that can be scheduled for a less hectic day.

If you have the approach of ticking all of them off in a single day, great. In a hypothetical world, it will work. In the real world, however, you will always be running short of time, no matter how hard you try. Thus, an ideal approach should be to try to accomplish the ones that require urgency first. Failing to do so will leave you with a mix of some important and unimportant tasks accomplished with some of both remaining. Imagine, if you got all the unimportant tasks accomplished and fell short on completing any of the ones near a deadline? You don't want to be in that fix now, do you?

Identify any three to five MITs that you must, no matter what, complete by the end of this working day. Even if you have, say 15 to-dos on your list, you would still have at least three or five completed.

On the other hand, if you multitask and spend your time, effort and resources tackling, say 10 in a day, you might only complete a few and still have many incomplete. Which approach do you think will make you feel more accomplished and proud?

Why does it work?

To some entrepreneurs, productivity is getting a lot done in a day. For some, it is getting things done consistently. The first entrepreneur is concerned with the numbers on the spreadsheet, whereas the other one focuses on consistency in those numbers. Both these mindsets have their pros and cons, but I live by the second approach. I aim for steady progress, even if it means less work. Achieving speed isn't my biggest goal, but rather progressing continuously. Do you see the difference? I am more concerned with whether I am moving any closer to my goals or just handling each obstacle as it comes.

To put this into practice, I tackle the most important task first thing each day. Sadly, I learned this the hard way. There were days when I spent the most crucial hours of my day ticking off the 3rd, 4th, or 5th task on my to-do list instead of accomplishing the important ones. It took me time to realize that not only did I need to reorder my to-do list, I also needed to get the most important ones out of the way first.

Why you may ask? Look at the remarkable benefits:

Crowning willpower

It is proven by science that our decision-making ability and willpower are the highest first thing in the morning. As the day passes, we see a decline in both and thus might end up making poor decisions. Knowing that, wouldn't it be best if you get done with the most important task first?

Fewer distractions

Morning is a peaceful time. You have just woken up, haven't had to go through the nerve-wracking traffic or listened to your secretary dictate your schedule for the day. And the biggest perk… There are no emails whatsoever waiting to be checked, replied to, or spammed. Now correct me if I am wrong and suggest you tackle MITs first thing.

Builds Impetus

MITs are usually the most boring and challenging tasks. Getting them off of your to-do list will leave you with the less important or boring ones. Besides, when you are done with the bigger chunk, the smaller ones seem easier and accomplishable. There is a chance that you may end up completing more than you had anticipated.

How does it work?

Makes sense, no? But how will it play out in reality? Great, you have made up your mind to work on MITs but how do you identify one from the uncountable tasks on your to-do list? Here's a simple formula that I follow. There are only three steps to it, and each will take you less than a minute to sort through.

The 3-minute Trick to Identify MITs

Step 1: Start With a Second List

Not a second list but making another smaller one from the one you already have. A lot of times we overestimate the number of tasks we can accomplish in a day. Generally, there are 3-5 tasks one can feasibly accomplish in a day. So what are the top priority tasks that you wish to get down with by the end of the day? Knowing that is the first step.

Step 2: List them by Order of Urgency

The second step involves organizing those tasks in a sequence. Which task has the most beneficial outcome? Arrange them by order, and you now have an order in place to start working with.

Step 3: Just Do It

Not technically a step, the goal is to start right away. Start from the top and work your way through. Don't skimp on things or try to multitask. Only move forward once you are done with the task at hand.

Chapter 2: Handling Emails and Saying No When Appropriate

It's Monday again. As you sit at your desk you sense a sinking feeling in your stomach. You know that the moment you open your laptop, you will be flooded with hundreds of emails just waiting to be opened.

If you are in charge of a large team, chances are that you will easily receive 10-plus emails first thing in the morning. Been there and done that, as they say. Going through each, sorting them, responding to them, forwarding some to others just seems like it's going to take all day.

And then a thought hits you... You didn't become an entrepreneur just so you would be bombarded with emails all day. You became an entrepreneur so that you could head a successful business. But what about the inbox and those pending ones from yesterday and the day before that? What about all those emails that need to be responded too?

What if there weren't any? Hypothetically speaking, what if there was a world where there were no emails to be sent, forwarded, or replied to?

Well, why hypothetically?

In this chapter, we are going to aim to get your email list to a zero. We will talk about the different techniques you can use to prevent the bombardment of emails and, more importantly, stop them from piling up.

Secondly, we shall talk about another damaging habit that entrepreneurs have—saying yes to things that aren't important. We shall learn to say no and also why it is crucial for you and your business's growth.

Habit 3: Getting Your Email List Down To a Zero

To achieve success, you first need to know the definition of the word success. Similarly, if you want to achieve a zero inbox, you need to understand what it truly means. The term inbox zero was coined by Merlin Mann, productivity guru. Despite common belief, it has nothing to do with the number of emails you have in your inbox, instead, it is about regaining control over the monotonous practice of email checking.

Most of us spend a good amount of hours checking emails and responding to them. Even when it isn't a part of our job description, we are accustomed to checking them periodically in case something of top priority comes along and requires action. And in case we get busy elsewhere, there is a pile waiting to greet us the next time we go online. The piling of unanswered emails can stress you out in no time.

If a majority of your emails begin with "Sorry for the late reply," then it means you have a problem that needs to be resolved.

Why Achieving a Zero Inbox is Crucial?

But why is it this crucial and what good comes from it? For starters, an inbox zero relieves you from the stress of wasting important time that can be utilized elsewhere.

Even when there isn't any email requiring an urgent response, they still need to be backlogged for future references. According to research, this can cause a psychological drag. This means that we lose mental focus and clarity.

Secondly, when we are checking our emails, we have the habit of opening at least three to seven before actually taking action on one of them. This practice not only delays response time but also adds to your stress in case a new email pops-up. Once you are done replying to it, you go back to each open tab and reread the email, losing precious time.

A zero inbox eliminates this waste of time and helps you to learn how to go through each message just once. This leaves you more time to be productive in other areas of your work and also meet deadlines.

Next, with an inbox zero, you don't overlook any important emails and they surely don't get buried in the pile of reading emails. You achieve this by sorting out each email in separate folders based on their urgency, whether they need to be addressed or not, or do they need to be saved as a reminder for some later date or not.

This way, even if your mind fails to recall an important task you were emailed about, you can always go back to the folder you placed it into and remember it in less than a minute.

A zero inbox also prevents procrastination, which is again a possibility when you have too much on your plate. We discussed earlier how an overload of work can demotivate one to start. It happens with an overcrowded inbox as well.

Finally, when you achieve a zero inbox, there are no pending unread emails in your inbox. Can there be any relief bigger than that?

Zero Inbox and Improved productivity?

On average, an entrepreneur is exposed to 126 emails per business day (sent and received) in 2019. Among these, many need to be responded to urgently. Moreover, the same study also reveals that we spend approximately 11 hours per week sending and receiving emails (Email Statistics Report, 2015-2019, 2015).

Although designed as a productivity enhancer, email reading can sometimes become a source of distraction and loss of focus. Did you know it takes a person about 23 minutes to get back to the work they were doing after responding to an email? If you are constantly wasting that much time after every email, how are you going to get any work done at all during the day? Despite trying to avoid the "bing" of a new email or a pop-up on your desktop, we just can't resist the temptation of opening it, can we? In a way, we are a lot like Pavlov's dogs who were conditioned to salivate when the bell rang. Even when we know that in doing so we are deliberately making our minds suffer the psychological drag and waste time.

It's Difficult but Possible

If you are aware of Greek mythology, you must know the Hydra. The magnificently scary creature with nine snakeheads—cut off one and in its place grow two heads. Managing an inbox today is similar to battling a nine-headed Hydra. Every time you think addressing this last unread mail will free you up, two more come along popping.

So maintaining a zero inbox seems quite difficult but not impossible. Hey, if Hercules can do it, so can you! Here's how you are going to succeed at it.

Assess Your Inbox

First, just take a clear and thorough look at what's in front of you. Don't touch or open or address any email, just browse through the list, dates, sender and subject lines.

Once you have a mental note prepared, ask yourself the following questions.

What type of emails are you receiving the most? Is it junk mail, messages from social networking sites, newsletters from subscribed websites, or messages from the boss or colleagues?

What is the date you received them? Are they months old or just arrived a few hours back?

Who's repeatedly messaging you? You must have some regulars who keep asking about every little detail.

What are the subject lines like? Are they offering info right away or luring you with click-bait titles?

This identification will not only help you with the organization of your inbox but also help you develop a plan of action on which to address first and how. Furthermore, it will help you recognize where you're lacking and help you fix it. For example:

If you receive more junk mail, then it is a priority issue.

If you receive emails from one or two senders only then it is a communication issue.

If you receive most emails on Monday, then it is a scheduling issue.

Unsubscribe and Spam

The next and most important step to achieving a zero inbox is spamming and unsubscribing to emails that are nothing but time-wasters. It will take a few hours to get the job done, but it will save you hours moving forward. The clutter needs to go so that you are left with a less stress-causing inbox and deliver timely responses and use the remaining time to work on MITs.

Here are examples of some of the types of emails that you must receive regularly.

Emails from colleagues and clients

Emails from customers and well-wishers

Emails from people you never respond to

Newsletters

Social media alerts

For managing the first three categories, use folders and labels. Folders and labels allow you to easily sort your emails and reach out to them immediately when needed. When naming your folders, be very thorough as you don't want to make it yet another unmanaged folder like your inbox.

For every email that you receive, whether from your clients, customers or well-wishers, ask yourself if you need to address them immediately or not. Next, decide on a course of action. If you don't plan to respond to it right away but say you will in a few hours, place it in the folder titled, "Need to respond to."

If you think that waiting a little longer, say days or weeks, won't make any difference, place it in a different folder titled, "Respond Later." If you have the time, let the sender know that you plan on responding but would appreciate some more time.

Adesh Silva

The last two categories can also be managed using the same technique; however, I want you to have full control over them and come out as a conqueror. Remember, we are trying to defeat the Hydra here?

Newsletters

You might not even remember when and how did you subscribe to them. Of course, they are from websites you know or stores you love to visit but why do they keep sending you this newsletter about how well they did in the last quarter, what new things are happening at their end and what new products are being promoted.

If you ask me honestly, I will tell you to unsubscribe to all of them right away but before I turn into the bad guy here, you need to ask yourself three questions to decide their fate.

How often are they opened by you?

How often do you read them after opening them?

How often do you use them? Do you save it for later reading, but what they are promoting or write down the coupon numbers for future use?

If you don't have an answer to any of these, unsubscribe and delete it. If you love the brand/business, you are going to buy from them, with or without a reminder from them.

Social Media Alerts

This is a combination of emails you receive from your social media accounts in case you use the same email ID to log in on them. These include emails from Facebook, YouTube, Twitter, Instagram, Spotify, Skype, Pinterest, Snapchat, Medium, LinkedIn, etc. A majority of these just remind you of redundant information as someone commented on your post or your tweet was retweeted this many times, etc.

For starters, if you are managing a business, it is best to keep your professional and private IDs separate. If you can't, as so many people now have this ID as the only means of a link to you, go into the settings of each of these social apps and turn off the email alerts.

Habit 4: Learn to Say NO to Things That Add No Substantial Value

Don't kids love to say the word no to everything? Honey, finish your vegetables. NO! Wake up, it's time for school. NO! We have to go to the doctor's appointment. NO! It's time for you to stop playing and go to bed. NO!

It seems effortless, right? It's because they are solely concerned about what they want and how they feel. And then we are introduced to all these emotions, feelings, and thinking about others' crap. Well, technically not crap but saying yes to everything does complicate things, doesn't it?

As we grow older, the word "no" seems like a distant memory and "yes" becomes the order of the day. No day goes by when we don't do things just to please people. And it stems from the fact that, deep down, we all want to be liked and appreciated by others. So we end up doing things that we wouldn't have initiated on our own had someone not asked us to do.

For an entrepreneur or magnate, whose primary job includes persuading others to buy their products or services, people-pleasing is an important skill to have. It's because you are risking your stakes in the hope of earning some profits and to do that, you have to chase after every opportunity that comes along the way. And how do you do that? By engaging in contact with others, offering a few favors here and there and other similar modes of convincing. This strategy does work when you are just starting, but after some time you might find yourself overcommitted and exhausted.

What we entrepreneurs forget sometimes is that doing business isn't a race. It involves working smart and not just hard. Your time is valuable and thus should only be utilized on things posing utmost urgency and enticing revenues. Therefore, saying no to things that don't add any value whatsoever to your life or business is not just acceptable but a necessity.

Why Entrepreneurs Love the Word "Yes"

To learn how to say no, we must first learn why we say yes so often? More importantly, why is our thought process?

Studies reveal that there are several reasons entrepreneurs just can't risk saying no.

Entrepreneurs are chasers: Entrepreneurs are chasing after opportunities all the time. After all, what's the point of running a business if you aren't doing that, right? This is one reason why they always find themselves double or triple booked.

Entrepreneurs are hard to please: Since they are thinkers and doers, they are always thinking about the "What's next." They are never content with what they have, and they are always looking for ways to do things better.

Entrepreneurs are risk-takers: Again, true. That is the whole point of building an empire. They are more likely to dive into projects quickly and thus often end up with more than what they bargained for.

Why You Must Excuse Yourself?

Although it may seem hard to turn down something of value, there are some side-effects of overbooking yourself on tasks and projects. The truth is, there's always a limit to what you can do and failing to meet the committed deadlines will only harm your rapport with clients and customers. Moreover, you will waste valuable time doing something that doesn't have a promising return and feels burnt out. An exhausted businessman is no use to anyone.

Furthermore, if you don't say no to things that don't guarantee a substantial advantage, you risk losing your focus. Becoming a people pleasure can land you in shallow waters as you may make decisions that benefit no one—not your company, employees, or yourself. A lack of focus will havoc your business standing and you may even fail to meet your original goals.

Have you ever met someone who builds a business around someone else's idea or suggestions? How well did they do? Your ideas fuel your business. You can never be a successful entrepreneur if you aren't passionate about the thing you do. It has to come from within you. Thereof, say no when required, without feeling guilty because at the end of the day, it is your investment, efforts, resources and time.

How to Say No To Things with No ROI?

The majority of entrepreneurs rush headstrong into the business world with a to-do list and tons of expectations. Coming armed like this makes it difficult to say no. What they need is a to-don't-do list so that they can make wiser decisions. The key here is to learn when it is okay to say no and when letting go is the best option. Here are some great ideas to put into practice to get you started on this new journey of saying no.

Seek Answers from Within You

Time is the most precious of resources and a successful entrepreneur knows that. The bigger you get, the more people you will come across seeking favors and requests. If you have a difficult time deciding and evaluating whether to say yes to their request or not, ask yourself these important questions listed below. Believe me, you will have your answer in no time.

Does it benefit your company's image?

Does it excite you?

Do the efforts outweigh the outcomes?

What is your gut feeling about it?

It is aligning with your core business objectives?

If you mentally answered yes to all these, you know it is a task worth taking. If any of the projects you take up don't drive your business toward success, are they worth investing your time in?

In the words of Adam Grant, a bestselling author, and professor, "Saying no frees you up to say yes when it matters most." (Grant, n.d.)

Change your attitude

Aspiring entrepreneurs often have a scarcity mindset. They think that if they say no to any opportunity coming their way, it may never come again. The worst thing about this kind of mentality is that you also end up saying yes to clients who aren't worthy or a good fit. Suppose you fail to meet their expectations due to overload at work, not only did you waste your time on them, but you also have to live with a bad word of mouth through them. Thus, opt for an abundance mindset instead. The abundance mindset suggests that good clients are abundant out there, you just need to wait until you find them or they find you and save your best for them.

Aim for focus

Steve Jobs, in an Apple Worldwide Developers Conference, once said, "People think focus means saying yes to the thing you've got to focus on. But that's not what it means at all. It means saying no to the hundred other good ideas that there are. You have to pick carefully. I'm as proud of the things we haven't done as the things I have done. Innovation is saying no to 1,000 things."

This means that you have to be wise to choose the things you want to invest your time into. Sometimes, you just have to be a ruthless time manager. This is important because only when you value your time, you will be able to focus on the more important tasks and prioritize them. After all, they are what will take your business forward and help you achieve your long-term goals.

When you say no to unwanted clutter, you are saying yes to more important goals by reserving your time and mind for them.

Chapter 3: Dealing with Time Wasters and Living by the 80/20 Rule

In chapter 3, we shall learn about what time wasters are, how to overcome them and what does it mean to live by the 80/20 rule for an entrepreneur. Most entrepreneurs struggle when it comes to prioritizing their tasks and end up wasting precious time over unnecessary time wasters. To help you, choose better and wiser, you must first learn what they are and whether you have been indulged in them without intention or knowledge.

Habit 5: Dealing with Time-Wasters

What is a time-waster, exactly?

A time-waster is anything or anyone that detracts, distracts, distances or diverts your attention from something important such as your plans, appointments, events, goals or activities. Sometimes they are self-made and thus self-destructive. If I were to describe time waster as a person, I would call them smart. They lure you into their charm so effortlessly that you don't even realize where the time went by. It's like sitting through a really good opera concert and losing yourself completely in the aura and magic. However, the end isn't quite as applaud-able as you may feel frustrated, stressed, or overwhelmed afterward.

Time wasters also come in different forms and shapes. They can be a task, the environment, an appointment, a location, activity or someone you know.

No matter how much you enjoy indulging in them, they aren't good for the business. Lucky for you, they are predictive and thus, preventable. They can be controlled with better though processing and quick responding. Take a look at some of the most common time wasters in the life of an entrepreneur.

The 6 Most Common Time Wasters

1. Social Media Surfing

The biggest and most annoying time-waster is browsing the internet. There is always something shinier than the last picture, like a bigger diamond in the mine. Like most people, entrepreneurs too innocently waste too much time surfing the web, wasting time on a website unrelated to work. Social media not only distracts one from important work, but it also becomes a source of procrastination. You keep telling yourself that you will get back to work when the clock hits a certain time, but it never really happens. The next time you look up at your clock, the set time has already passed and you have no choice but to allow yourself a new time to close all those enticing tabs.

You must keep in mind that although it is nice to have an online presence when you are running a business, it isn't a necessity for you as the business owner. You can always delegate the job to someone to keep tabs on your business and research the needs of your customers and clients respectively. Your job is to ensure that the work gets done and the suggestions posted online are turned into a reality for better customer experience.

2. Busy Checking Messages

Checking your emails now and then chews up your time like anything. Not only that, but it also distracts you from far more important tasks. According to research, business owners check their emails 30 times per day. And since we already established that it takes one 23 minutes to get back to working again, you can imagine the amount of time lost doing meaningless work.

3. Accomplishing Routine Tasks

Many entrepreneurs, ignited by the fire of excitement, take up more than what they bargain for. They are the ones handling the finances, marketing, production, and sales of the job. It is okay to take responsibility for most things, but it is against the principle of working smart. What they don't realize is that while they are trying to multitask, they are losing enormous amounts of time doing mundane tasks that can be delegated instead.

To identify these time-wasters, make a list of all the tasks you perform in a day. Once you have the list identify all those tasks that are delegable such as running to the suppliers and getting your supplies delivered, assigning teams in the production department, managing the social media channel to answer queries, personally responding to all emails received, etc. etc.

Next, create another list of the most important tasks you must accomplish. Tasks that only you can do, tasks that require your expertise and knowledge such as dealing with clients. Do you think that there is no one capable of dealing with the routine tasks? If there is, delegate it to them and capitalize on the time that is now free. Utilize that to refocus your efforts on the most important tasks so your business can generate better revenues.

4. Switching from One Task to Another

Another hurdle entrepreneurs face when hoping to manage their time effectively is thinking that multitasking is beneficial and smart. They can't be more wrong as switching between tasks only keeps you distracted and unfocused. And any task completed without focus isn't going to cut—at least not in the longer run. So stop checking your email when working on an important worksheet as you might not like the price multitasking comes at.

Always try to get things done within a set timeframe. Once a task has been accomplished give yourself a 10-minute break and then start on the next one.

5. Traveling for Trips

If you are just building your startup from scratch, you might be tempted to travel to every happening seminar and conference. I won't lie, I was too! The temptation to be in the same room with your competitors, the other big names in the industry and to get a chance to introduce you and your brand to them is just every aspiring entrepreneur's dream. It took me some time to realize that the trips were unnecessary as most of the highlights from big workshops and seminars are placed on the internet a few days later. So if you come to think of it, you aren't missing out on a lot. Now imagine you spent that time elsewhere, such as building your brand, meeting new prospects, making important calls? Wouldn't that help your business better?

CPSIA information can be obtained
at www.ICGtesting.com
Printed in the USA
LVHW051206101220
673819LV00032B/1626